HERMAN CHARLES BOSMAN

A CASK OF JEREPIGO

Herman Charles Bosman

A CASK OF
JEREPIGO

HUMAN & ROUSSEAU
Cape Town   Johannesburg

FIRST PUBLISHED IN 1964
SECOND EDITION PUBLISHED
BY HUMAN & ROUSSEAU IN 1972
FIRST IMPRESSION 1972
SECOND IMPRESSION 1974
THIRD IMPRESSION 1978
FOURTH IMPRESSION 1980
THIRD, COMPLETELY RESET EDITION
FIRST IMPRESSION 1991

Copyright © 1991 strictly reserved
Published in uniform edition in 1991 by
Human & Rousseau (Pty) Ltd
State House, 3-9 Rose Street, Cape Town
Typography by Cherié Collins
Cover design by Patricia Going
Cover illustration: "Jeppe Boys High"
(detail) by Dan Swart
Set in 11 on 13 pt Zapf Book Light
and printed and bound by
National Book Printers, Goodwood

ISBN 0 7981 2885 2

Contents

Herman Charles Bosman
A Man Who Never Unmasked

Regarding history, Herman Charles Bosman put "the poet's embroidered lie" above the carefully authenticated factual account. He was not only more willing to hear the first than the second, but readier to believe it too.

So far as a history of Bosman's life is concerned, I am aware that a kind of poem would get much nearer to the plain truth than this outline of the bald facts.

For the events of Bosman's life were only fuel to the triple-flamed fire of his imagination. The outward meaning of anything he underwent or did is seldom an accurate reflection of what it meant to him. How things struck him is suggested in three features of his personality: he was a romantic, he was a humorist, he was a rebel against many of the commonly accepted values. Most of us assume these attitudes now and again, feeling as if we were on holiday a bit from our serious selves. But Bosman was all three of these things consistently. If romance, humour and unconventionality were the features of a mask, it was a mask he never put off.

And as the world never saw Bosman without this "mask", I believe he never saw the world save through it. That is the point I want to make: that Bosman had a way of seeing life which was very much out of the ordinary – perhaps uniquely his own. Life in his vision was crowded with things that fascinated, delighted and awed him; with secret meanings that kept him vibrating in a vital way. As a result his personality was invested with an aura of intense excitement. And that is the keynote of his life.

He was born on the 5th of February, 1905, in the village of Kuils River near Cape Town. Soon afterwards his family moved to the Witwatersrand and settled in Johannesburg, where Herman and his younger brother, Pierre, were educated, at the Fairview Junior School, Jeppe Boys High School and the Witwatersrand University and Normal College. Their father worked as a miner and lost his life in a mine accident during Herman's youth.

By his high school days already Bosman had revealed his absorbing concern with literature which set a bias to everything he did. In his studies he was drawn to languages, at which he excelled, while science and mathematics repelled him. In his matriculation examination he answered the paper on algebra with a beautifully phrased essay explaining that he felt he might dispense with a knowledge of this subject since his ability in English was exceptional.

Having contributed prominently to the school magazine, at the age of 16 he began to write a series of amusing storyettes, original in conception and polished in execution, which were published under the pen name "Ben Eath" in the *Sunday Times*, whose editors remained unaware of their contributor's youth for a good many months.

It was the school library, naturally, rather than the playing fields, that attracted him. Here he went one day to peep curiously at the work of the notorious agnostic orator, Robert G. Ingersoll, about whom he had been hearing, and was overwhelmed by such magnificence of *style* in the first few lines he read that he was immediately converted to atheism which he professed to the end of his schooldays.

Also in this library he came upon the daguerrotype portrait, the potted biography and the works of that vision-tormented man, Edgar Allan Poe, and the impact of this discovery reverberated through his life. His sense of Poe's mastery never diminished. And it is a fact that the American's life story finds many strange echoes in Bosmans's.

The Elizabethan drama and lyrical poetry and the poetry of the Romantic Revival also first engaged his attention during his youth. It was Spenser's *Prothalamion* that he recited aloud atop a mine dump to cure himself of a severe boyhood stammer. Possibly it was during his early years, too, that he made the acquaintance of the works of Oscar Wilde, and even Baudelaire, Rimbaud and Verlaine (for whom his feelings were mixed) and of the American humorists and short story writers of the later nineteenth century.

Although Bosman's interests, his sensitivity and his individual, oblique mode of thought would tend to set him apart, especially at school (he said once that his mother had imposed on him "the gloomy grandeur of genius"), he never became the studious recluse. Reticence on many topics was always part of his make-up, but his love of fun, his vivid imagination and his extraordinary vitality precluded him from other forms of reserve. He burned with a desire for experience of all kinds and bold, even defiant, in his adventurousness, he earned himself a reputation for wildness.

Picaresque escapades marked his career at high school and college. He had no interest in politics but associated with the members of a political youth organisation which, in these intense times shortly after the rebellion of 1922, exercised itself in such promising activities as pamphlet posting, street processions and mass meetings. He dispelled sobriety from the manner of these earnest pursuits, introducing a note of fantasy and extravagance. He led a nocturnal pamphlet posting raid as a result of which the walls of the Normal College buildings were thickly plastered with propaganda – the inside walls. At a meeting on the City Hall steps which one of his friends was addressing he chose to lead the heckling and caused the gathering to break up in a state of riot. During the disturbance he was felled by a blow from a lemonade bottle. Later he told his friends that on looking in the mirror next morning he had read the words "Australian Mineral Water Works" stamped across his brow.

At the University he was solemnly awarded the third prize for his entry in a students' poetry competition and then revealed that the successful piece he had submitted was written by Shelley.

In the meantime he was writing in both verse and prose.

And then, when Bosman was still a student, a casual meeting of merrymakers in the streets of Johannesburg one Christmas Eve, when the celebrations of the crowds, who milled about the heart of town waving their paper switches and calling their greetings, had a romantic carnival quality, led to his marriage to Vera Sawyer.

On receiving his degree Bosman was appointed to a teaching post in the Groot Marico district. His wife, deeply attached to her mother, did not accompany him. But this year on the platteland was a most fruitful one. The place and its people enthralled him, and he spent much of his time listening to the reminiscences and lore of the farmers he visited and provided himself with the background of his best-known work, the Oom Schalk Lourens stories as well as the "Voorkamer" sketches that were published in *The Forum*.

At the end of the year he returned to Johannesburg for the Christmas holidays, a visit which culminated in catastrophe. His mother had remarried; her second husband was a Scots widower with grown children of his own. It was to their house that Bosman came for his holiday; and this was the setting one night of an obscure disturbance, a clash of personalities which terminated in Bosman's firing a hunting rifle at his step-brother and killing him.

The Old Magistrates' Court was the scene of the preliminary examination which preceded Bosman's trial for murder. The brightness of the moonlight at the scene of the shooting was one of the questions on which the court heard evidence at the trial which resulted in a conviction and the imposition of the death sentence. On the judge's recommendation, however, a reprieve was granted and at the age of twenty-one Bosman went to serve a four-year term of imprisonment with hard labour. He chronicled his prison experiences fifteen years later in his unique novel – realistic, unforgettable for its powerful depiction of horrifying and pathetic happenings, and yet pre-eminently a humorous book – *Cold Stone Jug*. In similar strain, in two of the sketches included in this volume, he wrote on the Old Magistrates' Court, protesting against its proposed demolition. In prison he wrote the first of his Oom Schalk Lourens stories.

On his release Bosman was given lodgings in the town rooms of Mr. Willie Bloomberg, a dental mechanic who was a great lover of literature and had a fine gift as a raconteur. To his friend Bosman dedicated his volume of poetry *The Blue Princess*, describing him as "The Ex-Republican who found a King".

The Blue Princess was produced on the printing press of which Bosman became part owner with a remarkably colourful group of journalists and authors. They brought out another volume of Bosman's poetry as well, *Jesus*, under the name he now commenced using, Herman Malan (Malan was his mother's maiden name). These two books contain some of the finest lyrical verse written in South Africa. Here is one of the pieces from *The Blue Princess*:

Lies

I flung at her feet small prophet's truths,
I who bestrode the firmament to steal
God's trembling blaze of jewelled lies,
Of blue, wild dreams in Paradise.
I flung at her feet small truths –
(A stranger laughs with my beloved's eyes).

It was at her feet I cast those things,
At her feet those little truths,
But I forgot
That her heart lay
On the grass.

This little book and another collection, *Mara*, which appeared a few years later, also contain in their introductions what are, to my knowledge, some of the boldest statements ever made in print by a poet about himself and his work. In later years when I knew Bosman, part of his creed, and something that was strongly expressed in his bearing, was that an artist must have humility. The note struck in those prefaces may be described as one of defiant arrogance, the artist's fierce world-spurning aspiration to immortality. When I read for the first time Bosman's claim that his poetry had achieved a poetic "finality" hitherto only approached by Baudelaire, which was why "I know Baudelaire belongs to me even more nearly and intimately than Isaiah and Keats belong to me," it was the contra-

11

diction that was irresistibly brought home to me. I decided that some tremendous and terrible experience in the intervening years must have changed the writer of those "audacious boasts" into the man I knew. To an extent I was right, I discovered. But now I know that it is not just as simple as that. Bosman and Herman Malan are not two separate men with contradictory qualities and attitudes who replace each other as time passes, but one continuing personality in which many paradoxes are somehow reconciled. Perhaps it was on the grounds of another part of Bosman's creed that these reconciliations took place, namely (and I have expressed it already in other terms) that the obvious was to be eschewed, in what one said and did, as well as in what one perceived.

From this printing press also came Bosman's remarkable pair of pamphlets in defence of Daisy De Melker, and a number of short-lived journals he helped edit and to which he contributed stories and poems. One of these was *The Touleier*, one of the most richly laden and interesting literary magazines that have appeared in this country. The others, *The New Sjambok* and *The New L.S.D.*, also carried literary items, but achieved notoriety by aiming at a character for lurid sensationalism. As a result they faced public and official protests, a succession of libel suits and finally banning.

This was also the period of *The Rolling Stone*, a mimeographed literary quarterly edited by Bosman's friend Edgar Bernstein, to which he contributed.

Visiting the Johannesburg Public Library one day about this time Bosman overheard and was deeply impressed by the voice of one of the library assistants who was serving a borrower. So strange was the girl's utterance that Bosman felt that no-one in the world could ever possibly understand her. Her name was Ella Manson. The flamboyance of this strange, strong-looking girl's personality matched that of his own. She was brilliant, imaginative, energetic, fiercely individualistic. Like him she was imbued with the urgent sense that life was to be lived, not contemplated or "prepared for". He said of her that her art was Life, but she had specific artistic gifts as well. A powerful mutual attraction sprang up between them, and

12

when he learnt of her pianistic ability he insisted on her accompanying him to Europe to seek a worthy teacher and possibly a concert career.

Events had not been kind to Bosman's marriage with Vera Sawyer but despite this and the fact that she now released him so that he might marry Ella, she remained a close friend of his until the end of his life.

He married Ella and the two departed for a nine-year sojourn in Europe.

London, Paris and Brussels were the chief scenes of the vicissitudes they passed through. They faced the Paris winter in near destitution and London's rains with broken shoes. They marched in street processions of a fresh political character, and they visited the tomb of Oscar Wilde, as a result of which Bosman wrote one of his best-received essays.

They were also, for a while, the owners of a successful publishing business they had founded, the Arden Godbold Press, which brought out books for the few of taste. It was Ella's ambition to render her husband financially independent of work for life, and the business was conducted uncompromisingly with this end in view. A young parson whose collected verse had been rejected by Arden Godbold threw himself to his death under the wheels of a train. It must have become clear that something in the lives of Bosman and Ella was similarly being sacrificed to their profit machine and at last they abandoned it.

In the main, though, Bosman worked as a journalist. He was the drama critic on a London paper when T. S. Eliot's *Murder in the Cathedral* was first produced, and condemned its chilly intellectualism. He saw in the work of its author and his followers, self-consciously anti-romantic and serious, the deplorable decadence of English letters – a decline which was checked, in his view, with the emergence, in later years, of Christopher Fry.

In London Bosman met and talked with the late W. W. Jacobs, whom he held to be an undervalued genius. And in London he wrote a number of the stories afterwards collected as *Mafeking Road* and sent them to Bernard Sachs, his former

13

school and university classmate, who was editing the *South African Opinion*. (It is possibly not the least unconventional of Bosman's actions that, a South African writing abroad, he should send his work to be published in his native country.) This magazine also published poems and essays from Bosman's pen, but much of what he wrote before about 1940 will never be known, for he once deliberately abandoned a pile of his manuscripts on top of a cupboard in a London hotel.

Shortly after the outbreak of war the couple returned to South Africa. They lived in a flat in central Johannesburg and their life seems to have had a certain sombre smouldering quality. Ella played a silver-painted piano and wore clothes and make-up designed to give her a hard, unprepossessing appearance – certainly not one that bespoke her as the woman of culture and sensibility she was. Bosman worked as a journalist and advertising space salesman (work he hated, although he is said to have been one of the most successful "spacemen" ever to tramp the pavements of Johannesburg) and made unpredictable and uncharacteristic forays into political activity, writing letters to newspapers and pamphlets and disconcerted most of his acquaintances.

During this period *Mara* appeared. It contained a strange play or dialogue on the nature of love, and some poetry. One long poem is called "Ellaleen" and its opening lines are these:

I sing of the morning I who have seen
Only the afternoons.
My westering heart is sunset-stained
But white where the languorous lips had been
Of Ellaleen.

About 1943 Bosman went to Pietersburg as editor of the local newspaper. Here he met Helena Stegman, a schoolteacher of great sensitivity, sympathy and understanding. When, shortly afterwards, his marriage with Ella was wound up he married the gentle Helena who shared the last eight years of his life.

In 1944 Bernard Sachs revived the *S.A. Opinion* which had run for four years in the 1930s. Bosman, reverting after a while to the use of his own name, was the literary editor and contributed stories and poetry, art, film and literary criticism (the individuality of his style and approach renders all his unsigned contributions unmistakable) as well as the series of essays and sketches collected in this volume.

The literary editorship of a South African monthly journal, however, did not provide Bosman with a living. He did subeditorial work for the *Jewish Times*, sold space, and even took a teaching post at the private college where Helena was employed. But he found attempting to introduce aspiring matriculants to a sense of poetry a terrifying task and soon gave it up. It was the principal of the college, Dr. Damelin, who introduced me to Bosman, who accepted me as his private pupil in "literary techniques" – a course which proved to be, in more ways than one, the most profitable phase of my education.

For Mr. Colin Rheed-McDonald and Die Afrikaanse Kulturele-leserskring Bosman translated the Rubaiyat of Omar Khayyam into Afrikaans, and in connection with a scheme for the translation of other classics, he went with Helena to Cape Town in 1948. The project, however, went awry and they were back in Johannesburg after a few months.

In 1945 Bosman had been invited by the Afrikaanse Pers Boekhandel to adjudicate in their English novel competition. The first prize was shared by Daphne Rooke, for *The Sea Hath Bounds*, and the late Charlotte Elizabeth Webster, for *The Expiring Frog* (both novels were afterwards well received abroad). He thus came to meet Mary Morison Webster, sister of the dead authoress, herself a fine writer and possessed of visionary and imaginative gifts which could not fail to appeal to Bosman.

Late in 1946 A. P. B. brought out Bosman's novel *Jacaranda in the Night*, a difficult and problematical book, but one whose extraordinary literary and visionary qualities still await the appreciation that is their due. The following year the Central News Agency published *Mafeking Road*, which was recognised as an important contribution to South African literature, and has been repeatedly reprinted to enjoy what I believe to be the greatest success earned by a purely literary book published only in South Africa. The stories were broadcast on the B.B.C.'s Third Programme under the auspices of Roy Campbell, who often expressed his deep admiration of Bosman's work, and some of them have been pirated and published in countries behind the Iron Curtain. In 1948 A. P. B. published *Cold Stone Jug.*

In 1949 Bosman resigned from *S.A. Opinion*, which had merged with *Trek*, and from *The Jewish Times*, and became a proofreader for *The Sunday Express*. At the same time he commenced his "In die Voorkamer" series of humorous tales about life in Groot Marico which appeared regularly in the weekly journal *The Forum* whose editor was Mr. John Cope and literary editor Miss Lily Rabkin. During the busy period that now commenced he also did other writing and started working on a new novel which was found unfinished when he died, besides a large number of poems in manuscript. The following, from a poem called "Arrival", is representative of the startling beauty that abounds in these verses:

An angel with one shaded wing spoke
Too nearly of sin;
I breathed into my lungs the smoke
That Troy and Gomorrah had gone up in.

And look at this short poem called "Learning Destiny":

One last look at your hills, Lysander,
With the purple of grapes
And of blood and the undermost waves of the sea;
There was only one story
That was so honey-filled with glory,
So gangway-full of murders, laughters, rapes –
And I, with the restraint on me
Of the Christian's God, was a bystander
When a new world was born
In the reaping of yellow corn
And the treading down of green corn.

About the begining of 1951, having lived in at least nine different places since their marriage, the Bosmans acquired the house at Lombardy East on the outskirts of Johannesburg which they intended to be their permanent home. They had always been felicitous party-givers (their parties, which came once or twice a year, were always superb occasions on account of the conversation) and in October they invited their friends to a house-warming. It was a party as splendidly gay as any in its tradition, but by the time the guests departed their host was little more than a day from his death.

He died of a stroke on the afternoon of Sunday the 14th of October.

I knew Herman Charles Bosman during the last five years of his life. Upon me, and I believe upon many others (possibly even all) who knew him, he exercised an enchantment (I use the word aware of all that it suggests relative to magic) of extraordinary power. This charm, which was capable of becoming a really large thing in the lives of those it affected, was one of the special phenomena of Bosman's personality. What did it consist in?

It had nothing to do with ordinary urbanity. Bosman's positive horror of the obvious and pedestrian made him shy away from "serious discussion". When a topic was broached for polite investigation "But look . . ." he would exclaim, pressing his knuckles nervously to his lips; and then, enthusiastically pounding his thigh, he would bound off into some joke or fancy wildly at a tangent to the track of the leaden-footed frivolity.

Related to this were his extraordinary sensibilities which rendered him susceptible to disturbance by things that leave most people unmoved. As unpredictably as he might be delighted, I felt, so unpredictably might he be distressed, with a distress that sprang from his instinctive vision of what things really mean. Spiritually and intellectually I leaned very heavily on him, but I regarded him also, somehow, as a delicate child, a fearfully susceptible "sensitive plant" to be shielded from the crude impact of things. There was always a sense of the miraculous in the thought of his being *here* in Johannesburg, walking these tramlined streets, riding in lifts, sitting behind type-writers. (It was with a peculiarly affecting excitement that I began to learn the fantastic story of his life. To me it was fantas-tic, somehow, that there should be a story to his life – that time should have propelled him earthily into the present out of somewhere else.)

Whence then that enchantment? Well, it was the effect on the positive side of the qualities I have just described. It was due to what can only be called the superlative *sweetness* that informed Bosman's personality, supplemented by the "liter-ary delight" of his conversation.

He was the gentlest and most genial of men, unsurpassably warm in human feeling. He resembled Oscar Wilde, not only in the length of his lifespan, his conversational brilliance and social attractiveness, but also in humanity and kindliness. It was he who told me, with a touch of awe, how Wilde had taken off his coat in winter and wrapped it round a beggar. But he had the capacity for equal and greater generosities. It was Bos-man who, on visiting a man who had been committed to an asylum for the insane, declared that so far as he could see this man was saner than the doctors and keepers who had charge of him, and then took this man into his own home and found him a job of work at his own side and in all respects restored him to the fullness of life which he enjoyed for as long as Bosman lived. And the benign and tender spirit of that was to be felt in all of Bosman's human intercourse while I knew him – in fact in his dealings with all living things, human, animal and even vegetable. And with it all, making it into sweetness, went laughter: the hugest laughter and the hugest things to laugh at were always in process in Bosman's presence. So that we cannot think of him without thinking of laughter.

But laughter already has to do with the "literary delight" of Bosman's company that I have mentioned . . .

To Bernard Sachs I owe this tale about Bosman at a perform-ance of the Laurence Olivier coloured film *Henry V*. The scene was the field of Agincourt. The English bowmen had formed their line and were holding the flight of their arrows until the moment when it would be most terrible. And down toward them came thundering the French cavalry – visors down, banners fluttering from the ready lances, all colour and rhythmical motion – in that glorious charge that grew minute after minute in excitement, grandeur and pathos. And suddenly Bosman rose from his seat, threw his hat up into the bioscope air, and yelled at the top of his voice "Vive la France!" The audience roared with laughter.

And that is exactly what used to happen with Bosman all along. His fancy used to play right round things, giving them an extra dimension, for him giving them their reality. Anything his imagination could not get around did not exist for him. He accepted no abstractions at second hand. That is why sharing his conversation was always such a vital experience. Everything said was personal, spontaneous and brand-new. Most of the time the room would be thunderous with laughter – a laughter which was only the happier and freer because you felt you were in the presence of a cosmic moment when the boundary of human experience was being rolled back in some special way, for you were laughing at poetry. The division between the sublime and the risible was gone.

And that is where the remarkable pieces that go to make up this volume come in. It is these sketches that come closest of all his works to conveying an idea of the flavour of Bosman's conversation. And it is especially this part of his work – though by no means must anyone undervalue the delicious fun in the Oom Schalk Lourens and "Voorkamer" stories in this connection – that ranks Bosman as a humorist of the first order, on a level with those great Americans of the last century, Mark Twain, Bret Hart, Ambrose Bierce, O. Henry and the rest of that wonderful school whom Bosman considered to be the Elizabethans, the true Golden Age *poets* of American literature.

When Bosman's literary career was broken off while it was still gathering momentum, South African literature, like a Baudelairian albatross, was suddenly deprived of soaring flight and reduced to a solemn, pedestrian, limping thing with a pipe in its mouth. To those who knew him personally there was another way in which his death also seemed to be the interruption of a strange and wonderful white-winged flight.

19

As I have intimated, most of the material in this volume appeared in *S.A. Opinion* and *Trek* from 1944 to 1949. With very few exceptions the pieces were printed under three successive general titles, "Talk of the Town", "Indaba" and "Pavement Patter". Frequently they were not given individual titles, and where these were lacking I have supplied them.

The piece called "My Life" was published in a magazine of the typographical workers' organisation, having been written only shortly before the author's death.

The two pieces which close this book – the essay called "Humour and Wit" and the obituary tribute to Stephen Leacock – contain all that might have been said about Bosman's approach in a more critical introduction and give Bosman's own views on the field where he raised a unique and bounteous harvest.

June, 1957 Lionel Abrahams

My thanks are due to Mr. Leon Feldberg for permission to reprint material from *The South African Opinion* and *Trek* and to the staff of the Johannesburg Public Library, Reference Department, for making their files of these magazines available to me for copying purposes.
L.A.

My Life

A vein of humour is supposed to run through a good deal of my writings. The worst thing about a joke is that it can as easily as not fall flat. It is also no novel experience for me to have people laughing themselves sick over something that I've been genuinely in earnest about. What all this is leading up to is that I wish to express it as my conviction that, contrary to popular opinion on the subject, about the most insuperable social, financial and cultural handicap there is in life is for a person to have a sense of humour. "Laughing when things go wrong": that's incorrect sequence. It's *through* laughing that things *go* wrong.

I was born in Kuils River – a Cape Peninsula village within sight of Table Mountain – but I have lived most of my life in Johannesburg. My links with my birthplace are of the slenderest. Some years ago, yielding to a nostalgic impulse, I paid a visit to my old home town. It had changed but little since I had last been there as a child. From the train I recognised the church. The railway station was still the same galvanised iron building painted yellow. But there was nobody in the place that I knew or that knew me. Still, Kuils River is only a small town, and after I had signed my name and it had got around who I was, I had quite a lot of notice taken of me. For people all thought I was related to Bosman, the rugby forward. I didn't feel called on to tell them I wasn't. I did not want my home town to get disillusioned in me.

I grew up in Johannesburg. In my youth I had frequently to listen to old men's stories of the early days of the Rand. This sort of thing: "I knew Jo'burg when, where the Corner House is today, there was just a tin shanty." Or: "Many's the time I sat on a flat stone on the veld, eating biltong, where there's today the Public Library." Elderly pioneers used to derive a great deal of satisfaction from indulging in that sort of talk, which used to bore me, at the listening end, stiff.

And it's a strange circumstance that today few things annoy me as much as the sight of young persons yawning when I recall how I used to eat polony in the bluegum plantation that is now Orange Grove. Or when I tell them that I can remember how, at the back of the Tech, there was the Old Tin Temple, with a dilapidated hobo leaning against it. (For many a long year the Tin Temple has been but a memory. The hobo is still there.)

The younger generaton today is, to my mind, a shade thoughtless. Too wrapped up in its own day-to-day affairs. I mean, I can remember the C.N.A. when it was a low, rambling structure, like a shed, and there was a fresh-faced stripling inside called William Wolpert.

I spent the best part of a decade, up to and including the first year of World War Two, in London. I was also in Paris and Brussels a good bit during that time. No, I didn't meet anybody great, or famous or distinguished. I saw hardly any of the places frequented by tourists. I was too busy trying to earn a living. One thing I'll say about London: it's a marvellous place to write in – in the winter months of the northern latitudes, when there is no sunshine to distract you, and each night is a dark tunnel of long, splendid hours, in which your imagination has free reign.

I was educated at Jeppe High and Wits. I learnt some of my most valuable lessons, though, at the educational institution conducted by Adversity (upper case "A").

Talk of the Town

The other night, in the company of a friend, one George, I sauntered out into the streets of Johannesburg. We strolled slowly as we were deeply in thought; and we spoke of this and that. We were not in search of adventure, ours being no more than a purposeless ramble through the streets and along the night and under the stars: and we all know, of course, that a sauntering in this style can never be purposeless.

And in our stroll George and I discovered, in Johannesburg streets, flowing with night, O. Henry.

And we came to the realisation, then, that through whatever streets one walks, in whatever city in the world, the hour being after midnight, then whatever happens, the people one encounters and the adventures that befall one – these have all been created by the master hand who invented Baghdad-on-the-Subway. And New Baghdad. In the streets of any city the Caliph Haroun-al-Raschid walks abroad, when the hour is after midnight, and you can tell by the incredible nature of the adventures that come his way that the Caliph has emerged not from between the hashish-laden covers of the Thousand and One Nights, but out of the Four Hundred Club, or, if we must continue the lisp in numbers, out of the pages of The Four Million.

Anyway, George and I ambled forth into the streets of the city of Johannesburg, and after a glance at the sky, to acquaint myself with the hour, I was satisfied that the realms through which we made our way was pure O. Henry. And the world of O. Henry is different from the kingdom of Edgar Allan Poe and Dupin and the detective thriller. Because the night is so much less young. But it could by now be the country of Phrygia, with Apuleius excitedly explaining that we have come all the way through Camathrace, and that we have traversed many a mountain road, and have crossed many a frontier, and, lo, we are in Phrygia "where things are no more what they seem".

23

But there is this difference. In the world of O. Henry all things are always what they seem. They are things that have always been like that: And throughout the world they have never changed.

The magic about the things in the world of O. Henry is that they are what they are. The people in this world are what we always knew them to be. That is their romance.

Anyway, George and I made our way down Plein Street, and we passed the Carlton Turkish Baths, where we had earlier that same evening called on an old friend. And we had spoken about old times together. For it is right, when one meets an old friend, that one should talk of old times. I spoke of an article which I had written long ago, and which my friend had, of course, forgotten: but he was polite enough to say, yes, he remembered it; he couldn't recall just exactly what it was all about, of course – something about an old Eskimo custom, was it? Or wasn't it about somebody who had an operation? – but he remembered it, of course. And then he told us a little story about a matchbox. And he asked after a man we had known in the old days, somebody who sang.

But that had all been earlier in the night.

Now George and I proceeded along Plein Street. And we turned up towards the station. And in front of the Transvaler Building we came across a long row of rickshas, drawn up beside the pavement, and facing the open square of the railway goods depot. The ricksha boys had all gone home. I trust that they had all been a-bed these many hours; else would they not be in fit condition to pull their rickshas, when the daylight brought them business in the form of gramophones and suitcases and bunches of many hues, and a drunk or two, perhaps, and battered bedsteads, and bundles of magazines for bulk postage, and beehives.

Yes, the ricksha boys had gone home. But we encountered a man who had not gone home. He was leaning against the middle ricksha in this long line of rickshas. He was a square-built man dressed in a brown suit. At first, judging inaccurately from his posture, we thought that he might be a client for a ricksha. We thought that perhaps this man was standing there, waiting through the long night hours for the dawn, when a ricksha boy would come on duty and convey him to his place of residence – if the man in the brown suit was still capable of remembering his place of residence.

So George and I approached this square-built man in the brown suit and we began to hold converse with him. And so we learnt that we had been wrong in our first surmise.

"You are waiting for a ricksha, sir?" I enquired of the stranger.

"No," he answered, "oh no. Not at all. I am an Eastern Province man."

That, of course, explained everything. We felt that being an Eastern Province man implied a great deal. An Eastern Province man, for instance, would not be so lacking in foresight as to come and stand there, waiting hour after hour through the night, just so that a ricksha boy should chance to come by some time after dawn and then proceed to convey this man to the Eastern Province. We felt that if a square-built Eastern Province man in a brown suit had elected to journey back to the Eastern Province by ricksha, he would have made all the necessary arrangements in the way of advance booking, and so on. He would have fixed up beforehand with the boy as to where he was to meet him, and at what time. An Eastern Province man wouldn't have left things like that just to luck; and a lonely vigil in front of the centre ricksha in a long line of rickshas.

George and I were abashed.

"Of course," George said, "that explains it. Now we know. You have informed us that you are an Eastern Province man."

Shortly afterwards the man in the brown suit withdrew from our company. He proceeded in the direction of the open square of the railway goods depot, leaving me and George standing in front of the ricksha line.

There was a car parked in this square. And while George and I watched him, the Eastern Province man did a very singular thing. He opened the near door of the car and got in. Then he closed the door behind him. We thought he was going to drive off. But, instead, he opened the far door. And then he got out, on the far side. And he slammed the door shut behind him, and he kept on his way, skirting the side of the Transvaler Building.

And at that moment a number of men emerged from the darkened doorway of the Transvaler Building, and they made straight for that car and got in. George and I went up to these men. They had obviously been working late on the *Transvaler* newspaper. But they were too well dressed to be journalists. And when George and I began to hold converse with them, we realised that they were also too well spoken to be journalists.

So we were satisfied that these men were linotype operators and machine minders and other members of the printing-work staff of the *Transvaler*. We acquainted them with the singular conduct of this Eastern Province man in the brown suit, and one of their number said, "Well, what else did you expect?" From which remark George and I judged that the speaker's place of origin was the Western Province.

We felt sad when this car drove off and we realised that, through having wasted time in idle talk, we had lost sight of the man in the brown suit. George and I felt that, going on his behaviour so far, this man might yet be able to lead us to something.

But we never caught sight of him again. We followed him, of course. And we kept on his trail for many blocks. But we went only on information supplied us by people we encountered in the streets at that late hour. A watchboy would tell us which direction this man had taken. Or somebody on his way to start work on some unearthly shift would impart information to us. Or we would hold up a passing lorry, and the driver would tell us, yes, there was somebody answering to our description about two blocks further down, and proceeding in a northerly direction.

Our questions would always be the same: "Have you seen an Eastern Province man in a brown suit, going up this road?"

And the reply would invariably be the same: "Well, I can't say for sure if it was the Eastern Province man, but I did see a fattish man in a brown suit, and he was walking in such and such a direction . . ."

But we never caught up to him again. And afterwards George and I lost his trail. We gave up the chase when we got this piece of information from a truck driver we had followed up:

"Yes," the driver said, "I did pass a man. But I didn't come across anybody like that. I only passed a white-haired man with a girl."

"If he has got white hair, what does he want a girl for?" George enquired. This seemed a very sensible thing to say. And we agreed to abandon the chase. So we went and lay on a stretch of grass under a tree in Braamfontein, and we watched the railway engines chook-chooking up and down the line, belching flame and snorting like live things, and we regretted, with the introduction of electrification, the passing of the railway engine.

But I am afraid that this is getting us right away from what I was trying to say about O. Henry and The New Baghdad, and Baghdad-on-the-Subway, and the Caliph Haroun-al-Raschid. The point I have been wanting to make is that, after O. Henry's tales of night-life, us writers haven't got much chance in trying to tell stories about the life in a city's streets in the hours after midnight. And this applies to any city in the world. In *The Four Million* and *The Voice of the City*, O. Henry has covered the whole field so completely, and with such splendid artistry, that we who try to use the same setting for any of our stories today, know that in the atmosphere we seek to create we are only patterning after the master.

We can still have a shot at the streets of a city before midnight. We can stil give that a go, yes. But the main gate of the palace opens after 12.01 a.m., very furtively, to allow the Caliph and his Grand Vizier to make egress. And from that hour onwards the streets of a city belong to O. Henry.

I have thought of the predicament of a scribe in the Middle East city of Baghdad today, and he an Arab who writes only in Arabic, and has never heard of American literature. And he will write a story about Baghdad after dark, and the Caliph will come into the story, after midnight, a real Caliph in the real Baghdad. And this writer will send the manuscript to the editor of the local Arabic literary journal. And the editor, being more widely conversant with world literature than this writer, will return the manuscript to him, referring him to exactly that same story that appears (not so well told, perhaps), in *The Voice of the City*.

There are no more stories left for us writers who walk the streets of a city in the early hours of the morning. O. Henry has cleaned up.

But, as I have said, we stand a chance before midnight, before the witched hour. Then the women's faces do not yet stand flesh-revealed under the make-up; the powder is not streaky yet, nor the lipstick smeared. And the men are still cheerful or sombrely drunk: they have not yet reached that stage of wisdom, when the winey fumes playing about them are but wan and mocking memories. We who come after O. Henry, in our writing of the city streets have to leave before the twelfth stroke of midnight. We are but Cinderellas. We must hurry from the scene of revelry, lest at the striking of the fateful hour we are verminously revealed in our rags.

It is for this reason that the heading at the top of this page reads: "Talk of the Town," and not "The Voice of the City."

Street Processions

For as long as I can remember, almost, street processions have been in my blood. When I see a long line of people marching through the streets – the longer the line, the better I like it – something primordial gets stirred inside me and I am over-taken by the urge to fall in also, and take my place somewhere near the end of the procession. I have no doubt that the reason why, many years ago – before Communism had the social standing and prestige which it enjoys today – the reason why in my youth I joined the Young Communist League in Johannesburg was because that part of Socialist ideology which consisted of organising processions through the streets, holding up the traffic and all that sort of thing, made a very profound appeal to my ethical sense.

And it has been like that with me all my life.

There is something about the sight and the thought of a long line of men marching through the streets of a city that fills me with an awe that I can't define very easily. And it has got to be through a city. A procession through a village or just over the veld isn't the same thing. And the people taking part in it should be mostly men. One or two women are all right, too, perhaps. But there shouldn't be too many of them. Banners are optional. And while I am not too keen on a band, I can overlook its presence.

The ideal conditions for a procession are grey skies and wet streets. And there should be a drizzle. My tastes don't run to the extremes of a blizzard or a tropical downpour. Thunder and lightning effects are out of place. All you want is a steady drip-drip of fine rain that makes everything look bleak and dismal, without the comfortable abandonment of utter desolation. Then through these drab streets there must come trailing a long line of humanity, walking three or four abreast, their boots muddy and their clothes (by preference) shabby and shapeless in the rain, and their faces a grey pallor. They can sing a little, too, if they like, to try and cheer themselves up – without ever succeeding, of course. And in this sombre trudging – the dull tramp awakening no echoes – of thousands of booted feet on cobbles or tarred road, there goes my heart, also. I get gripped with an intense feeling of being one with stupid, struggling, rotten, heroic humanity, and in this grey march there is a heavy symbolism whose elements I don't try to interpret for fear that the parts should together be less than the whole; and I find myself, contrary to all the promptings of good sense and reason, yielding to the urge to try and find a place for myself somewhere near the tail end of the procession.

Oh, and of course, there is another thing, something I had almost forgotten, and that is the *cause* operating as the dynamism for getting a procession of this description organised and under way. Frankly, I don't think the cause matters very much. I have a natural predilection for an unpopular cause and, above all, for a forlorn cause – a lost hope, and whether this peculiar idiosyncrasy of mine springs from ordinary perversity, or from a nobility of soul, is something that I have not been able to ascertain. And so, while I always feel that it is very nice, and all that, if the march is undertaken by the participants in a spirit of lofty idealism, because a very important principle is at stake, I am equally satisfied, provided that the afore-stipulated conditions of muddy boots and grey skies are present, if the spiritual factors back of the demonstration are not so very high or altruistic.

This weakness of mine in the way of desiring to make one with street processions, identifying myself with and merging my personality in a mass of humanity moving onwards to no clearly defined goal, has in the past resulted in my becoming on more than one occasion involved in a considerable measure of embarrassment. In my youth, for instance, when the Salvation Army moved up from the town hall steps at the termination of a Sunday evening open-air meeting and I found myself marching on at the back, in a sort of trance, it happened at least twice that I followed the procession right into the Hope

Hall in Commissioner Street, with the result that, each time, I wasn't able to get out again until I had been converted.

And then, only a couple of years ago, with the annual Corpus Christi procession to the End Street Convent, when I had again from force of habit taken my place near the end of the line and was proceeding down Bree Street, feeling very solemn as I always do on such occasions, I realised, suddenly, the incongruity of my presence in the company of priests in black vestments and stoles and choirboys in white surplices, and all carrying missals, while I was dressed just in civvies and half a loaf of bread under my arm, which I was taking home for supper . . . as I explained to an abbot looking gentleman in a mitre, who hadn't said anything about my being in that procession, but who seemed unhappy, nevertheless, in a peculiar sort of a way.

Similarly, I have, at different times, marched through the streets of London with Communists, Mosleyites, Scotchmen on their way to the Cup-Tie, unemployed Welsh miners and the Peace Pledge Union.

The last time I marched in a procession was as recently as last Saturday afternoon. I was on my way home, when from the top of the Malvern tram I spotted in front of Jeppe Station a street procession in course of formation. I could see straight away that the conditions were just right. It was drizzling. The streets were wet and grey and muddy. The sky was bleak and cheerless. I prepared to alight. Unfortunately, however, the tram was very crowded, with the result that I wasn't able to get off before the Berg Street stop. From there I took another tram back to Jeppe Station, arriving there just as the procession was moving off. I took my place somewhere near the rear. We marched in a northerly direction and swung into Commissioner Street. Trudge. Trudge. Drizzle. Mud. Wet boots and shapeless clothes. I didn't ask what the procession was about. I didn't want to reveal my ignorance and chance getting sneered at. I had been sneered at by a procession before today and I don't like it.

"It's that (so-and-so) Steyn," the man on the left of me remarked by way of conversation.

"You're telling me," I answered.

He *was* telling me, of course. Otherwise I wouldn't know what it was all about.

"If it wasn't for him," the man on my left continued, "us miners wouldn't be on strike."

"Us miners wouldn't be," I agreed, relieved to have discovered, so soon, what the procession was all about.

A middle-aged man in front of me, in a khaki overcoat, was singing rather a lot. A young fellow with a free and easy sort of look marched next to him. On my right was a stocky man with a grey moustache and a red rosette.

"You know," this stocky, grey-moustached man remarked to me after a while, "in 1922 it was different. In 1922 I was shooting yous. In 1922 I was in the police. Now I am one of yous."

The imp of perversity inside me egged me on to pick a quarrel with Grey-Moustache.

"How do I know that you still aren't one of thems?" I enquired.

Grey-Moustache's neck went all red.

"I am a rock-buster on the Crown Mines," he retorted. "There's half-a-dozen men in this procession as knows I am a rock-buster on the Crown Mines."

In this way what had at first promised to be an unpleasant incident was settled peaceably. Only, I couldn't help feeling that in the depth of his most secret sincerities Grey-Moustache was still one of thems. As the old saying goes, if you're once one of thems, you're always one of thems.

So the march continued in the grey drizzle. Wet clothes and boots and mud-splashed trouser-tops. A number of low songs were sung. Various obscene remarks were made. Everything was in order.

A big fat man in a black overcoat was acting as a sort of linesman for our part of the procession. They called him Oom Tobie. He was a kind of cheer-leader. He would hurry on until he got about fifty yards ahead of our rank, and then he would stand on the pavement and shout out the slogans. These were in the form of questions to which the procession roared out the answers. As far as I could make out, it all had a lot to do with the miners' democratic rights.

"Do we want Steyn?" Oom Tobie would ask.

"No!" the procession would roar. That seemed to be the right answer.

"Do we want the capitalists?" Oom Tobie would ask again.

"No!" would come the thunderous reply.

Then Oom Tobie would look sort of arch, like a schoolteacher trying to tip his class off as to the right thing to answer, with the inspector present, and he would shout out: "But – do we want democracy?"

I make the acknowledgement – and gladly – that a considerable proportion of the miners shouted "Yes!" But it was also a fact that an equal number would answer, with the same degree of determination, "No!" It seemed to me that Oom Tobie had not properly rehearsed them in their responses. He didn't seem to have given them the proper instructions on this point. I came to the conclusion that Oom Tobie wasn't himself too sure as to what was the right answer either.

Trudge. Tramp. Grey faces. Dirty songs. Everything was going very nicely. Then, near Delvers Street, somewhere, the procession came to a halt. Oom Tobie, water dripping from his black overcoat but his face beaming, came and made a further announcement. "The West Rand boys is here, now," he said, "and we are going up Jeppe Street. And when you get to the *Rand Daily Mail* building, stand there and boo your guts out."

Everybody, myself included, looked forward to booing his guts out in front of the *Rand Daily Mail* offices. But I don't know what good it did. There seemed to be only a few clerks and subs and typists looking out of the first and second floor windows, and at the first blast of all those raspberries they drew back and went and hid somewhere. But nobody appeared in any window of the works department. Thus, after twenty years in journalism, I was denied the opportunity – which had so nearly come my way – of telling a comp. what I thought of him.

It was after we had passed the *Rand Daily Mail* offices that I realised why the man in the khaki overcoat and the free-and-easy youth were singing more loudly than anybody else. By that time they were not only singing, but also staggering. They had a bottle of Jerepigo wine which they were passing backwards and forwards and from which they were taking surreptitious swigs. Grey-Moustache reported the matter to Oom Tobie. As I have remarked before, once one of thems, always one of thems. Nevertheless, I have rarely seen a man as indignant as Oom Tobie was at that moment. And I am sure that not even an underground manager had ever dressed down Khaki Overcoat and the free-and-easy youth in terms of vituperation such as Oom Tobie employed now.

"You are giving us all a bad name," he shouted finally. "Drinking wine like that out of the bottle, and in the street. And in front of the *Rand Daily Mail*, too. What if they had taken your photograph, drinking wine, when all the boys was booing? What if they got your photo like that in the *Rand Daily Mail* on Monday morning?"

"But we did boo, too," the free-and-easy youth explained. "In between."

"Won't you have a pull at the bottle, too, Oom Tobie?" the man in the khaki overcoat asked. "Just a small one, Oom Tobie?"

"Well, seeing it's you," Oom Tobie replied, "and because it's raining today – but not for any other reason, mind you – I don't mind if I just have a small mouthful. But don't let anybody see. Don't pass me the bottle until that tram has gone round the corner."

A few minutes later the procession reached the town hall steps and I made a dash for home. But as there wasn't a Malvern tram in sight, I sauntered into a pub. I asked for a Jerepigo. I found it was good stuff.

34

For me, the section devoted to Stone Age implements is the most interesting part of the Africana Museum, occupying the upper floors of the Johannesburg Public Library.

Rows and rows of glass cases filled with paleolithic axes and hand picks. And these things were made in the morning of the Stone Age, in the evening of the Stone Age, too, some of them.

It is not difficult, in viewing these exhibits in the Africana Museum, to recapture something of that sense of pride which the craftsman of a hundred thousand years ago felt in the production of a stone axe, flaked to a fine edge and rounded as accurately as though it had been drawn with a compass. Drawn with a Stone Age compass, that is. For in the ellipse constituting the cutting edge of a primordial axe there are various bends and curves which would meet with a geometrician's surprised disapproval.

But the predominant feeling I had was that with the passing of the Stone Age mankind began to decay. In these stone implements there is a diuturnity, a slow perpetuity, a timeless permanence which the rust cannot eat into. In the Stone Age man and time are one. "Eheu, fugaces" was written by Horace in the age of iron. It is not a paleolithic sentiment.

The average stone axe in the Africana Museum is as keen and untarnished by the gliding aeons as it was when the man who made it chipped off the last fragment of stone from its surface and ran his thumb over the cutting edge in a faulty ellipse. And the cutting edge is as keen today as it was then. I mean that if in those days it would take sixteen or seventeen well-directed blows with that thing to chop a snake in half, it would take just about the same number of strokes today. A snake is like that.

And in those days, when men were cavemen, it would no doubt have been possible, with half-a-dozen thumps with a stone axe, to have sliced off the top of an ancient wild turnip as neatly as with the blunt end of a flat iron.

What term did the men of that vast antediluvian epoch apply to their own era, which lasted over a million years because it was built in stone? They called it the Stone Age, of course. They said this is the Stone Age, and they said it with pride. "We are living in the Stone Age. A tree is no longer just something for us to climb up into, like a string of baboons. Today, with our instruments of the Stone Age we can chop down a tree almost as quick as a beaver can."

While there must have been, in the beginnings of the Stone Age, conservative greybeards who shook their heads at this new-fangled invention, saying that their ancestral fashions were best, and that you could have too much of this progress business, and what do you want to hunt a leopard with a stone axe for, when you have got teeth? – there were also those, with a vision beyond their own generation, who said, resolutely, "Stone has come to stay." And they were right. It stayed. It stayed a million years.

There is something about the thought of an epoch that lasted a million years that calls forth our veneration. There is about it none of that showy evanescence of Rome or Tyre, whose sway could be counted only in centuries.

With the passing of the Stone Age there vanished for ever a splendid and ennobling era in the story of man. With it there must have gone, too, something of man's spirit; something of his faith in the eternal truths of the world. And my sympathies go out to that man of the Stone Age, who, being shown an implement made out of that new substance called iron, placed it on a tree trunk and struck it a mighty blow with his stone axe. It was a stroke that only a Stone Age man could deliver.

"This iron stuff is rubbish," he said.

"They manufacture junk nowadays," he said, holding firmly on to the useless handle from which the stone head had been splintered in a hundred pieces.

These were all foolish thoughts, of course, that came into my mind in the Paleolithic Section of the Africana Museum. It was pure folly, too, my imagining that decadence came into the world with the passing of the Stone Age.

Then, as if in confirmation of something in which I no longer believe, I saw, in the next room, a number of iron spearheads. They could not be more than a few hundreds years old. But I knew they were spearheads only because the labels said so. There was nothing left of their original form and shape, these things manufactured out of iron. They seemed nothing more than a few stray slivers of rust.

And the Stone Age lives on.

The Old Magistrates' Court

A few days ago I stood in a spacious courtyard surrounded with dun-coloured walls. The doors opening into the courtyard were few but massive; the windows were covered with rusty bars. Many years before, when I stood on that same spot and looked at those barred apertures, I thought that they were like a woman's eyes, heavily fringed with dark lashes. Now they seemed to be simply like windows with iron bars stuck in front of them.

The place where I stood was the yard of the Old Magistrates' Courts, in Johannesburg. Today the building is no longer a courthouse, but is used as offices of the Governor-General's Fund and for other purposes. But they don't seem to have found any use for the yard itself, which for half a century was the temporary place of detention for the city's awaiting trial prisoners, Europeans and natives, men and women. Whatever was the charge against them, those accused of transgressing the law were brought into the yard of the Magistrates' Court. They came on foot, handcuffed and under escort, or they were conveyed there by Black Maria.

Through the forbidding-looking portals opening on to New Street South the prisoners were conducted – quietly led, in most cases, cajoled or enticed, sometimes, or occasionally, simply pushed from behind – into the yard, there to remain until their cases had been disposed of. Which meant that they were either sentenced or acquitted in a summary trial by the magistrate, if the charges against them were not serious; or else they appeared on a preliminary examination, to be committed for trial at the Supreme Court.

It was warm and sunny, that afternoon of a few days ago, when I stood alone in that courtyard, at the beginning of a new spring, and I was surprised to find how little the place had changed. The walls had always seemed just so dilapidated, with the same patches of weathered plaster, yellow like old parchment, and the same extensive areas of exposed and discoloured brickwork. There seemed to be still the same cracks in the dirty grey of the cement floor: those fissures might have widened and deepened a little, with the years; but I couldn't tell. They seemed just the same, anyway.

And the blue enamel basin, fixed to a wall under a tap, was invested with that peculiar sort of squalor which becomes imparted to all inanimate things that have for long lived very closely to the raw things of human life.

The place had not changed. The walls were redolent of yesterdays that had lost their bitterness; they breathed of spectral long-agos, of ancient, sullied things.

The only way in which the present differed from the past – in which this afternoon was not the same as some other, vanished, afternoon, when the same sun shone down on brick and stone and concrete – was that now the prison yard was silent. But it was not an oppressive stillness. It was a tranquillity charged with a spirit of gentle melancholy, like when a single late violet is left growing on a bank where a little while before there were a myriad clusters.

And as in the perfume of violets, in that quiet there was a heady fragrance, maddening to the senses, so that that prison yard seemed to come alive again, for a little while, and the fat gaoler seated in front of the heavy door, in the far corner, was not a ghost but a stony reality; and the native warders were again marshalling their charges, making them stand up or sit down in rows; and the white prisoners, if they were new to the ways of a gaol, were clamouring at a little barred window about getting messages sent to their friends for bail – to the cynical amusement of the police and the old offenders, who did not expect to see the outside world again for many years, if at all, and who had other, more serious concerns. And a couple of street-walkers were once more looking into the cracked piece of mirror over the blue enamel wash-basin, putting paint on their lips and then wiping if off again, uncertain as to what would make a better impression on the magistrate who was to try them for soliciting.

For a little while, because of the silence pervading that yard which for 50 years had been a prison and was now open to any member of the public to stroll about in, there resounded once more within those walls the clank of fetters. In that dilapidated yard there was awakened again, for a few moments, that sombre activity of men and women languishing in bondage that is more stark than the dilapidation of crumbling plaster. Deserted of its tenants for ever, the yard in the Old Magistrates' Courts, for the first time since it was built, did not seem to be derelict.

I would recommend the artist or the writer, or any man or woman who is interested in that strange and brooding and carnal-twilight thing that we call "atmosphere" to pay a visit to this place. For I don't suppose it will be long, now, before they pull those old buildings down. And remember, as you walk the yard and your footsteps echo because of the silence, that there are ghosts from the past that walk beside you.

And for a few moments may the place come alive for you also.

The glint of the spring sunshine on the handcuffs. On tarnished people and on dreams that have gone. The gaudy scarf which a man will wear around his neck only a little longer: the scarf is shortly going to be replaced with a rope. The stained handwriting on the letter from his sweetheart which the forger pulls out of his pocket, surreptitiously – gloomily wondering why there is such a thing in the world as handwriting. The blue haze in which a native prisoner is puffing at a dagga-cigarette, in the lavatory while his accomplice watches the door. The crimson lipstick on the mouth of the harlot, as vivid now as it was twenty years ago. And the corpus delicti. And the placid clouds in the sky overhead. And the detectives. And the pallid terrors in the hearts of men.

As for me, I found, when I eventually turned to depart, that the massive door, because it moved so heavily on its rusted hinges, refused, for a few moments, to open.

A Visit to the Zoo

Last week a party of intelligent sightseers, which included the writer, paid a visit to the Johannesburg Zoo. We arrived at the main gate of the Zoo shortly after 10 a.m., so that we had plenty of time for securing a position of vantage from which to view the main spectacle of the day: for the primary purpose of our visit to the Zoo, on the particular occasion, was in order to be there at feeding time.

We had often heard expressions of a certain order. (The reader is familiar with the sort of thing we mean.) It has become a household phrase, for instance, to say of something or other that it is "like the Zoo at feeding time". We wanted to find out whether the reality was as gruesome as what we had depicted in our imaginations. "Feeding time at the Zoo . . ."

Anyway, we were prepared for horrors, and it is sufficient to say that we got them.

We shaded our eyes with our hands and gazed intently in the direction in which our look-out man was pointing. Yes, he was right. Almost indiscernible at first against the dark foliage, but gradually taking shape as he advanced, cutting swathes of yellow grass with his sickle, was a keeper. We had sighted our first zoo attendant. I opened out my diary and, having consulted my watch, made the following entry after the printed words, "Monday, 19th":

"At 10.48 a.m. precisely we spotted our first keeper."

What we saw taking place before our eyes in the next few minutes can only be described as a study in the macabre. For the keepers, whose numbers had now swelled to over half-a-dozen, lay down in a group on a wide stretch of grass and from lunch-tins and brown paper parcels they produced a variety of prepared foodstuffs which they consumed with avidity.

It was feeding time at the Zoo all right. We took a number of highly important photographs.

One of our party took me to view a bird which he described

as the most incredible-looking creature he had ever seen. It took us some time to find this bird, who is in a cage all by himself near where they keep the snakes. We located that bird, eventually, and I have still got difficulty in believing that so fantastic a creature really exists. I couldn't find out his name. There wasn't a label on his cage, and I wasn't surprised.

This bird is about the size of a cockatoo and his body is black and his eyes consist of complete circles of red and blue and some other colour, each more unbelievable than the last. All the colours on the bird look as though they have been stuck on out of a child's box of water colours. And then his beak. Well, I don't want to exaggerate, but I shall simply say, off-hand and conservatively, that his beak is several times too large for his body. Between seventeen and eighteen times, I should imagine.

Finally, his beak is shaped something like a trumpet and is made out of a cheap kind of yellow cardboard.

I want to go round to the Zoo one night and steal that bird out of that cage and put him in a sack. Because then I want to go round next morning to Lopis, the bird dealer, and I want to say, "I have a bird in this bag, Mr. Lopis, that you might like to buy," and I then want to produce that bird from the inside of the sack.

And the possibilities are that what Lopis will say, after they have poured water on him to revive him, will be the name of that bird.

What shall I say of the higher animals at the Zoo, the monkeys, the baboons, the chimpanzees and the gibbon? Well, for one thing, a baboon can look you straight in the eye. And for another thing, the Zoo authorities should not allow visitors to stand in front of the monkeys' cages and laugh at their antics. A spectacle of this description is unutterably degrading, and the man or woman with an adult mind recoils from it. About the most terrible thing that can happen to a creature is for it to be deprived of its liberty. The sight of birds and animals in cages is a solemn sight. The Zoo should be no place for moronic mirth and empty horse-laughter. Let there be humour, by all means, that grandeur of humour wherein the soul meets

42

itself, face to face, like in a temple. In a Zoo there can be no place for low comedy. Where the animals come from there are no gutters.

I looked at the baboons in the Zoo – looking away at long intervals, also, in order not to embarrass them – and the feelings of which I was most strongly conscious were that the baboons were a people who were kindly and highly intelligent and very unpractical, and who were poor but had kingly qualities, and who, of all the people in this country, seemed most nearly to conform to a type of person whom I would be proud to be able to claim as a fellow South African.

As for the monkeys, what is their gaiety but a defiant mockery of the worst afflictions of this world? Animated by an irrepressible spirit of fun, which brings into riducule the bitterest circumstances of their chained adversity – are these monkeys not courageous? The triumph of the spirit over physical circumstance represents the supreme achievement of the noblest minds. On this basis we should have to seek very far to find companions of the spirit who are as sensitive as the monkeys, and as cheerful and as brave.

"The great will not condescend to take anything seriously," Emerson says in his essay on "Heroism".

We would do well to ponder the truth of this statement, in its relation both to life and to art.

Later on, when we were having tea in the Zoo Kiosk, it occurred to me that there would be something singularly appropriate in the idea of an animal of unusual design – such as the tusked boar, for instance – escaping from his cage at that identical moment and strolling along towards this area in which the public was being served with refreshments.

I thought I would have liked to be able to draw the attention of both strangers and acquaintances to the approaching warthog (or polar bear or Cape spotted hyena) and to remark with a studiedly judicious air "This looks like something that might have walked out of a zoo."

It is a theme, this, that admits of a substantial number of variations.

43

There is in the pleasure which we, as adults, derive from a visit to the Zoo an element of melancholy, also, at the thought of how different our feelings were when we first went there, as children, in simple awe of the elephants and the striped tigers and with no complexes.

But it is right that we should not be able to recapture the emotions which belong to a vanished past. It is right that there should be no artifice whereby we can restore to life a world that has been too long drowned in moonlight or that has been lost in dreams. That's one thing.

Another thing is that a zoo is a zoo and not a circus.

The Standard Theatre

The trouble with me is that I never know what is going on in the world. I do not keep abreast of the latest developments in the field of politics, commerce and industry, culture and finance and philosophy. Consequently it was only at the tail end of the controversy about the closing down of the Standard Theatre that I got to hear of what was happening just about two blocks away from where I work. Nevertheless, if anybody had come to me at any time while the arguments pro and con the closing of the Standard Theatre were in full blast, I would have been able to say authoritatively and at any time: "No, the Historical Monuments Commission will not place a blue plaque on the Standard." I would have said: "They will pull down the Standard Theatre like they have pulled down all the old buildings, theatres, gin-palaces, doss-houses, temples, shops, arcades, cafes and joints that were intimately associated with the mining-camp days of Johannesburg."

Because I know Johannesburg. And I am satisfied that there is no other city in the world that is so anxious to shake off the memories of its early origins. If other cities took the same pride in obliterating the architectural remnants of their past there would be no figured obelisk tapering by the banks of the Nile; there would be no Westminster Abbey with its dangerous fan ceiling, consisting of thousands of tons of masonry that curves down like Madeira embroidery: the visitor to Westminster Abbey walks carefully and softly, on tiptoe, almost, in reverence of the Abbey's storied past – and afraid that if he doesn't exercise caution the ceiling will come down; there would be no Erechtheum on the Acropolis, no tall columns beside the Tiber. No Zimbabwe.

No, they are not going to demolish the Standard Theatre because it is a menace to life and limb, because one day it might catch alight. Next to the Standard Theatre fire hazard, as I have said, I give you Westminster Abbey's tons-of-masonry-nine-centuries-old-fan-ceiling hazard. I give you – oh, well, it doesn't matter. We of Johannesburg know why the Standard has got to come down, and we know also that no power on earth can save it.

It was in this spirit that I paid a visit to the Standard Theatre premises a couple of days ago. I could see that nobody hanging around the doors of the Standard Theatre at that moment cared very much about the fate of the old building . . .

So I went into the pub instead. "Is this Frascati's or is it McCarthy's Beer Hall?" I asked of the bar-tender. It was something that had often puzzled me. The bar-tender's explanation was lucid enough as far as it went. "It's Frascati's Pub, Pat McCarthy's Beer Hall," he said. "If you come in through the Standard Arcade – that door there – then it's Frascati's Pub. If you come in through the Market Street door, then it's McCarthy's. Simple enough, ain't it?"

The bar-tender told me that his name was Mr. J. Hodder and that he had been in the liquor trade in Johannesburg for 43 years, and that he had never once been in court – not even as a witness. The history of the pub was interesting. It wasn't opened at the same time as the theatre, however. Mr. Hodder didn't know why. I would have thought that the pub would have been opened even before the theatre. But I found out the reason for this afterwards, when I was upstairs talking to Miss B, the caretaker, and she showed me a very early photograph of the Standard Theatre. The buildings on the other side of the passage-way in front of the theatre were erected at a date subsequent to the completion and opening of the Standard.

I left the pub by the Frascati door and went up the stairs to interview the caretaker. On her door – No. 64 – was a notice "Out between 1 and 2." So I knew she must be inside having lunch. Accordingly I turned the knob and walked in – but only for a distance of 18 inches, that being the length of the safety-chain attached to the inside of the door. That gives you an idea of Miss B.'s character.

After I had assured her that I lived on a farm on the Muldersdrift road and didn't require accommodation in the Standard Buildings, the caretaker undid the chain and we got talking. I promised her that I wouldn't mention her name.

The man who built the theatre was a gentleman named Scott, Miss B. informed me. He would have been able to tell me a good deal more about the early days of the Standard than she could, she said. It was a pity I hadn't come round sooner – say 20 years ago, or so, when Mr. Scott was still alive. She didn't mind very much about the proposed closing down of the Standard Theatre, she explained, but what she did resent bitterly was the distorted impression which the S.A. Broadcasting Corporation conveyed to the public with regard to the kind of entertainment provided by the Standard Theatre in the old days.

"To judge from what we heard over the wireless," Miss B. said, "it would seem as though they put on only cheap variety shows at the Standard. Nasty music-hall turns. What about when Margaret MacIntyre and her company, straight from Drury Lane, presented *Traviata* – in 1894? You've never heard about that before, have you? Neither in the newspapers nor over the radio. And what about other well-known companies that put on some of the world's greatest plays? I'll show you the photographs."

I accompanied Miss B. to an office in the Standard Buildings, where Scott and Mendelssohn (of Mendelssohn's Buildings) carried on their business in the 1890s. Miss B. showed me a number of photographs of stage celebrities of the last century – music-hall stars who played in the Standard when the gold paint was still new. But I was more interested in the furniture in the Scott-Mendelssohn office than in the photographs. High oak desks at which clerks had sat on tall-stemmed stools; the rusty old iron safe; bloomy, ponderous chairs and tables that had constituted the last word in Victorian business-house equipment.

Miss B. drew my attention to the photograph of a corpulent male actor. A high stick-up collar and plenty of bulging waistcoat and a jacket with straight, narrow lapels. A shaggy jaw, bull neck and low forehead.

47

Miss B. told me his name. And she added, in a low voice, "He was the handsomest man I ever knew."

And the light sigh she drew then seemed to linger on in the old office after we had gone out again and locked the door behind us.

Out of the Past

I walked down Commissioner Street, looking for L. E. Hart & Co., described as the leading Rand tobacconists. The address: 3, Barnato Buildings, "two doors from Jack Herff's." I couldn't find the premises. No Barnato Buildings. Certainly no Jack Herff. Then I thought I'd look in at Oliver & Co.'s Great Drapery Sale, "now proceeding, no regard for Cost but Prices to suit all customers, carpets, linoleums and blinds fixed without charge during sale." The only address: Pritchard Street West. I just couldn't find where that sale was going on.

Similarly, I was unable to locate R. Campbell's Grand Display of Season's Novelties, "in the newly-extended premises recently occupied by Messrs. Rogaly, with the greatly increased space at the corner of Pritchard and Loveday Streets." Equally unavailing was my search for Amm's New Grocery, Provision and Hardware Stores, Library Building, "to be opened on Wednesday, at 3 p.m., by W. Hosken, Chairman of the Johannesburg Chamber of Commerce, who will also give an address suitable to the occasion."

I knew, of course, that "Library Building" must relate to the old Library that used to be in Kerk Street. I knew, because the source of the information contained in the above paragraphs is Vol. 1, No. 1 of the monthly magazine, *Johannesburg Faces and Places*: date of publication, March, 1899. The copy was loaned to me.

It gave me a real sense of satisfaction, last week, to walk across the streets of Johannesburg with that old magazine under my arm. And a feeling of superiority to be able to plank myself down in a bus next to a person reading the current issue of the *Outspan*. Anyway, that is the whole story.

Was *Faces and Places* Johannesburg's first monthly magazine, I wonder? I have no means of telling. One thing I do know, of course, is that it was not destined – alack and wella-day – to be the last. It would be interesting to learn whether

Johannesburg Faces and Places carried on much beyond Vol. 1, No. 1, a queerly fatal set of symbols not infrequently appearing on the cover of the penultimate issue of some of the world's most nobly-conceived periodicals. Who is there, who has been in the writing line for any length of time, who has not before to-day contributed a lofty and inspiring serial, a literary master-piece, to some journal or other, only to have that serial ending suddenly, in mid-air, on the bracketed phrase "to be con-tinued" – because that magazine didn't come out after Vol. 1, No. 3?

But such thoughts sadden me.

Instead, I shall fetch a manuscript out of my drawer and walk down the street with it, and offer it to the Responsible Editor of *Faces and Places*, whose address, according to the imprint, is "at 24, Parker's Building, Market Street, Johannes-burg, P.O. Box 1136." Note the word "at". But I haven't the least idea where Parker's Buildings are, and nobody else seems to know, either. So I'll have to post the MSS. instead, to the box number.

The front cover design for *Faces and Places* consists of a tasteful arrangement of the photographs of the Rissik Street Post Office (which is still there), and the Stock Exchange (looks like the same building) and the Magistrates' Courts (half the facade still above ground, minus doors and roofs).

That gave me confidence that out in the streets I would find that some of Old Johannesburg yet remained. Maybe the old Faces and Places had not all departed. I skimmed through the magazine. There was a photograph of Markham's, corner Prit-chard and Eloff Streets. Well, we know that Markham's is still there. So I hurried to the O.K. Tea Rooms and sat down at a table on the balcony, from which I could look down at Mark-ham's, and compare it with the photograph in the magazine, quickly, before the building got pulled down. From the O.K. Tea Room I looked down on Markham's pavement. I studied the women walking around there. In their New Look dresses they were exactly like on the photograph in the magazine. And at that very moment a man on a penny-farthing push-bike swept round the corner. He had on a top-hat.

That made me think about men's fashions. How did we men dress in 1899? There were plenty of tailors advertising in *Faces and Places*. Like Joseph Rosenbaum, of Green's Buildings, Commissioner Street, Fit & Style Guaranteed. Or F. W. Lawrence, High-Class Tailor, 10 Rissik Street, next door to *Standard & Diggers' News*. Or J. Rosenthal, Aegis Building, 100 Commissioner Street, Livery & Breeches Maker, Gentlemen's Hosier, Est. 1889. But there was no tailor from those days still carrying on business in Johannesburg.

I tried ringing up a few of the telephone numbers appearing in the advertisements. But that didn't help much. Dialling numbers like 101 doesn't get you very far these days.

The upshot of it was that I went to see one or two present-day tailors whose shop-fronts had an air of tradition. In that way I came across a tailor who had been in business on and off since before the War (Boer War, that is). His shop had heavy and very magnificent-looking fittings, solid, mahogany-sort-of stuff. He had moved it all forty years ago from his former shop to these present-day premises, he said. I asked him about men's clothes in days gone by.

"They wore narrower lapels, didn't they?" I asked. "In the Gay Nineties? Boaters and bowlers, didn't they? Short jackets and three-quarter length stove-pipe trousers?"

The old tailor shook his head slowly and conservatively. "Men's fashions have not changed at all since I was an apprentice," he announced.

I happened to look down, while he was talking. I saw narrow trouser-legs of a flashy pattern above a pair of boots buttoned at the side. It gave me a bit of a turn to think that for fifty years he had been making the same kind of clothes for his customers and himself, with nobody the wiser. There's Joh'burg for you, I thought. Old Joh'burg.

I paged through the advertisements some more. Names and buildings and faces and places that had vanished for ever. But something familiar, too, here and there, oh, yes – quite a lot of that. Suddenly, a quarter-page advertisement of Heath's Hotel. Described as "the Premier Hotel of Johannesburg", 78, Pritchard Street, P.O. Box 343. Telephone 155.

Collecting a friend and his wife, I set off for Heath's Hotel. That shows how it pays to advertise. Only, we discovered that the entrance, now, was in President Street. We went in. We walked through the hall and a lounge and found ourselves at the end of a long passage. We sat down at a table in front of a door that opened on to a lot of pot plants. When the steward came for our order we showed him the advertisement in *Faces and Places*. Why did it say 78, Pritchard Street, we asked him, when the entrance was in President Street? He explained that the Pritchard Street entrance had been closed for many years. Nobody could come in through the Pritchard Street entrance these days, he said.

We ordered "Three Hatherley Whiskies". (We saw the advertisement in two colours on the inside back cover of *Faces and Places*, where it was described as "Now for the first time being offered to the public. Hatherley Whisky speaks for itself as a pure and wholesome article of consumption.") The steward scratched his head. He thought he had heard the name, somewhere, maybe. But he wasn't sure. At all events, he didn't think they had it in the bar. Nevertheless, he would go and ask. It sounded a lot like black market stuff, though, he said.

He went. While he was away, we spoke of the old days, wistfully. Then, as though to refute the steward's statement about the Pritchard Street entrance having been closed, a man actually came in from that side, picking his way through the pot plants with care. He went past our table and strolled the length of the passage. We realised then that some changes must have been made in the President Street entrance, too, long ago. Because the man didn't go out through the door by which we had entered. Hy went out, instead, through the wall. I forgot to say that he wore side-whiskers and a "Sirdar" bowler and a stand-up wing collar.

Johannesburg

Taken out of its ancient African context, Johannesburg is one of the world's newest cities. I don't know whether any of the old 1886 pioneers survive. Perhaps there are still here and there a few genuine pioneers, who came to Johannesburg with the first gold rush: it won't be at all extraordinary, because they all seem to have been remarkably tough. But there are any number of men and women living in Johannesburg today who were children in Johannesburg's childhood, and have seen the city change and grow and develop as they themselves, leaving childish things behind, have grown to a maturity which is already passing into a dignified or dissolute old age.

Quite recently I spoke to a gentleman who made reference to certain steps chopped into the sides of the railway cutting just off Twist Street. That was before there was a bridge over that part of the line.

"We had gone to school across the open veld, there, for several years," my informant said, "and then the Netherlands Company excavated that cutting and laid the tracks, and so we schoolboys had to dig steps of our own into the sides of the cutting, in order to continue with our education. I was the youngest of this group and the older boys had to help me up by pulling on my satchel."

This gentleman also informed me that those old steps, crudely carved by the hands of schoolchildren, had suffered much from erosion during the many years of disuse, and he didn't think they were there any more. But he still had the straps of that satchel in a suitcase, somewhere, he said.

"They didn't issue any certificates in that school," this gentleman explained, "so I kept those straps from the satchel to show my prospective employers that I had had a schooling. And I have still got those straps – just in case."

You can still come across lots of people who can tell you about the spirit that prevailed here in the early days when Johannesburg was a roaring, wide-open mining camp, in which every citizen was imbued with the one laudable desire of making all the money he could in the shortest possible time. It was an all-in-scramble with no holds barred. The place teemed with short-cuts to a gaudy opulence. Adventurers from all parts of the world heard that there was money going in Johannesburg, and they flocked here to get some. And through some of the quaint whimsicalities of the Roman-Dutch law, which was the basis of legislation in the Transvaal Republic, some ways of making money were regarded as being less legitimate than others.

Thus when members of a spirited fraternity, hailing in the main from Australia, alighted at Park Station and started getting busy with their luggage, their activities gave rise to a good deal of unfriendly comment. For the sole luggage that these gentlemen had brought with them were home-constructed sandbags which they wielded on the populace, left and right, with a singular effectiveness.

The members of this fraternity, perhaps not unjustly, resented the discouraging attitude which officialdom adopted towards their industry as an unfair discrimination, based on the fact that they were newly-arrived immigrants who still had to ask passers-by the way to the Stock Exchange or the Rand Club, when they wanted to go and look for customers. The point of view of the authorities seemed to be, "You can see for yourself that we impose no restrictions. You can do anything you like to a man in order to take his money off him. Only you must not hit him with your luggage."

Even today this seems an unreasonable sort of distinction to make. Not allowing a man from foreign shores to contribute his luggage to the building up of a new nation and a new culture.

And talking about culture, I believe that Johannesburg has got all those attributes, mainly in the form of very raw material as yet, which will enable it eventually to occupy a leading place in the world of art and letters.

I would like to put forward my naive views on this subject in such a way as to try and avoid, as far as possible, anything in the way of controversy. But I believe, frankly, that as a source of new cultural inspiration to the world Europe is finished. Europe has got a background of unrivalled magnificence. Almost every town and city of Western Europe is impregnated with ancient splendour. But as far as the spirit of the peoples of Western Europe are concerned, these are glories that have run to seed.

For this reason it is most depressing to find painters in this country – some of them not without a good measure of creative talent – slavishly following the tricks of technique which contemporary European artists are employing with an ever-increasing complication of subjective subtleties as a substitute for individuality. Nothing can take the place of the raw inspiration of life itself, expressed with all the strength of a creative personality. Nobody knows this fact better than the European artists themselves, who are not glad that their inner force has decayed, but who simply can't help themselves.

It is therefore all the more regrettable that our South African artists, as a whole, should have no clear sense of values in this matter. You can learn all the technique you like from Europe. That's what Europe is there for. But if you don't put your own spirit into what you paint, either because you haven't spirit of your own or because you don't know how to express it, then what you produce cannot be anything more than synthetic rubbish.

But I believe that this is only a passing phase with South African artists. They are not trying to meet Europe on her own ground – which in itself would be an impossible enough task – but they are actually trying to copy Europe on her own ground. And this is pure clownishness.

But this stage will pass. And I believe that after that South Africa, with Johannesburg as its cultural centre, will find itself in an era of inspired creation, sprung forth out of the passion of love for this country, when we shall produce art that will reach heights of real grandeur because the note it strikes is authentic, and whose beauty will endure because it is our own.

We have got everything for it here. What has already been achieved in Afrikaans literature is a fine augury for the future. America has produced Edgar Allan Poe and Mark Twain, two sublime literary figures whose true influence is being felt only today. But Africa has not spoken yet.

I believe that it is possible to see Johannesburg as it really is only when we view it as a place of mystery and romance, as a city wrapped in mist. Is there any other city that is less than sixty years old – and the origin of its name already lost in the shadows of Time?

People who were present at the christening of Johannesburg say that the town was named after the second baptismal name of President Kruger. Other with equal authority say it was called Johannesburg after Johan Rissik. Other candidates – and in each case their names are put forward on most excellent authority – include Christiaan Johannes Joubert, Veldkornet Johannes Meyer, Johannes Lindeque, and Willem Gerhardus Christoffel Pelser (the latter, possibly, because his seemed to be the only set of names that didn't have Johannes in it).

There are at least another dozen claimants. And you need have no hesitation in supporting any one of them. The evidence in each case is indisputable.

With its sky-scrapers, Johannesburg is today no mean city. These tall edifices of concrete and steel would look highly imposing anywhere, leave alone just being dumped down in the middle of the veld. But we still bear one or two traces of mining-camp origin. For instance, there is the Public Library.

Ghosts

I read a small news item the other day about a Cape Town gentleman who complained that his life was being made difficult for him on account of ghosts. His house was haunted, he said; his children were terrified and his servants were wanting to leave; how he felt about it himself was not revealed in the newspaper report; perhaps he didn't want to say.

I wasn't surprised at this man's servants reacting in that way, especially if they were Cape Coloureds or Malays, who are almost as quick as Zulus at detecting the presence of ghosts about a place.

Is there such a thing as a ghost, anyway? Well, I do know that I have never come across a ghost or any other kind of a spirit manifestation at an orthodox spiritualist seance. In fact, to a person who is afraid of ghosts, I would have no hesitation in recommending an attendance or two at a spiritualist seance, when whatever fears he might have in regard to the things of the spirit world would be dissipated for him, through his being brought to a sane realisation of the fact that there isn't such a thing as the spirit world.

But outside of a spiritual research meeting place I am not so sure about there not being ghosts.

I once saw a ghost on the Pretoria road. It was near where the road branches off to Robert's Heights. And it was round about midnight. Afterwards, when it wasn't night time any more, I was no longer certain that it was a ghost that I saw there. I began to think that it might possibly have been a native riding a push-bike across the veld and then riding it up the trunk of a bluegum and along some of the lower branches, doing the latter part of his ride with his head hanging down. I didn't watch what he did after that, because it was a lonely part of the veld, at midnight, and I thought that what I was seeing was a ghost.

It is for this reason that superstition dies hard. People just don't pause to reflect. They simply say, straight out, "That's a ghost," whereas, in actual fact, there is always a rational explanation for any kind of (apparently) ghostly phenomenon. What I saw on the Pretoria road, and what my imagination took to be a ghost, was nothing more than a native performing acrobatics on a push-bike. Oh, and I also forgot to say that his neck was about two feet long, and curved.

But it doesn't matter very much whether or not we believe in ghosts; because, in any case, we'll have ghosts with us always. And if not real ghosts, then, at all events, real ghost stories – which are, I suppose, even better.

What great ghosts have we got from the past? What pale phantoms are wandering by the monuments of Rome and Thebes, or gliding by the blackened stones that once formed part of Ilium's topless towers, or huddled by the ruins of Babylon and Memphis? Majestic spectres haunting history's deathless palaces – no, I can think of none.

I can think of no great ghosts from the long ago; ghosts that grip my imagination even as much as does the cycling native performing acrobatic feats off the Pretoria road. (Oh, and there is something else I forgot: from the waist downwards he was semi-transparent.)

From the Old Testament I can remember, off-hand, Saul's encounter with the ghost of the prophet Samuel. But in the frightening tale I am more impressed with the personality of the Witch of Endor than with Samuel's ghost. And with the Old Testament we are coming from the ghost to the ghost story. And it is natural, here, to make allusion to Banquo's ghost. And to the ghost in *Hamlet* – whose main significance for me is the fact that Shakespeare once played him. I have often wondered if the Elizabethan producers always picked out the more dud roles for Shakespeare: you know, jealousy and all that: anybody can write Hamlet, sort of thing, but it takes a real classy actor to play him.

Literature, of course – fiction – is packed full of ghosts. But fiction is different from history. At least, I suppose that it what an historian would maintain, ignoring, for the moment, the immortality that is in good fiction. Because, when all is said and done, it is not the dull fact, recorded in terms of historical truth, that is going to survive. If you wait long enough you will see in the end that historical fact, carefully checked up and audited by the historian, cedes place to the poet's embroidered lie.

In terms of one or other kind of sociological interpretation of history, there were potent economic factors underlying the events connected with Edgworth Hill and Naseby. But to a poet it is all a story about a princess and a crown under an oak tree and Rupert of the Rhine. And it is the poet's lying version that is accepted in the end. (This might not apply altogether exclusively at the present day, perhaps. But this is only because at the present moment we still have so many people in our midst with nineteenth century minds – writers who have not yet realised, as the scientists have done, that nineteenth century rationalism is out of date.)

I trust that the reader will forgive the above rather undignified commentary. It is rather difficult to write about ghosts and have your nerves completely steady at the same time. (And I have just thought of something else that was peculiar about that native cyclist on the Pretoria road.) The artist hasn't got any right to ridicule reason, when he himself has got all those other gifts. In the same way, I feel, sometimes, that it was an unworthy thing for Edgar Allan Poe to have written his sonnet "To Science" – when he had his own "summer dream beneath the tamarind tree". But somebody must have come and disturbed him there, like a man came and disturbed me, also, the other day. It was a man who spoke about Ecology (which I had never heard of) as though it was a highly important word. And I also thought that it was something important, at first. Because I didn't know how it was spelt, I imagined that he was talking about Echo-logy. And I thought it was very fine: something, I fancied, to do with the lore of echoes.

And an echo is very important. For the ghost is sister to the echo. An echo is music's phantom, sound's frail spectre.

And when I have walked near a graveyard at night, and I have found myself on the verge of getting panicky, thinking of ghosts, then I have been able to still my fears in a very simple fashion. For I have thought, "Are we not also but ghosts, all we human beings who wander on the earth? What are we who live, but ghosts who walk by day?" And I have sauntered past that cemetery in another sort of fear – in trepidation lest my presence should distress that other ghost that already haunts the tomb.

And when I would start running, afterwards, and fast too, grabbing tight onto my hat, it was just to let that ghost know that he hadn't got to worry about me at all.

I can see, now, that it is a good thing to be friendly with ghosts. A headless apparition in rusty mail and clanking armour; a slender shade trailing her diaphanous robes in a religious light; an ignorant kaffir riding upside down on a push-bike.

Because, when you start feeling friendly towards ghosts it is by an easy transition that you begin entertaining amicable sentiments in regard to human beings also. And you start acquiring the right kind of humility. And I feel, reading his sonnet "To Science" again, that this is something Edgar Allan Poe should have learnt also. You haven't been given a superior intellect – or what you imagine is a superior intellect – merely in order that you should look down on somebody who has not got your gifts, and who in his simplicity talks about Ecology. Rather should you try and lift him up. The chances are that he has got qualities of sincerity and moral character that you will never have.

Very illuminating truths emerge from our contact with the ghosts. Next time I go down to the Cape I feel I must try to get a glimpse of Van der Decken, still trying to get his ship into Table Bay. He has been trying to do that for over 300 years now; the legend of the *Flying Dutchman* is that he used blasphemous language, and for that reason he isn't allowed to get his ship into port. I should imagine that by this time the way he is swearing must be something awful.

"Let the ghosts go," Ingersoll said. "We will worship them no more. Let them cover up their eyeless sockets with their flesh-less hands and depart forever from the imagination of men."

But I can't agree with that. It is a very salutary thing to have ghosts about, enabling us to see ourselves and our fellow human beings as loitering "manes" also. This is always an important discovery to make. It is like when a convict, after he has served a long period of imprisonment, hears the prison gate clang shut behind him; and, walking out into the sunshine of the street, he realises for the first time that the whole world is a gaol.

And it is no doubt in recognition of this need that the men of olden time brought the great tidings of the Holy Ghost.

Playing Sane

I converse fairly regularly with a gentleman who was confined for a somewhat lengthy period in what was known in the old days as a lunatic asylum and is today called by the euphemistic appellation of a mental hospital.

"They are all barmy there," the gentleman informs me, "male nurses, schizophrenics, psychiatrists, paranoics, pathologists, homicidal maniacs, keepers and attendants." This statement did not strike me as a being particularly novel, nor this ex-patient's assertions as to the strain that was imposed on him in his trying to preserve his mental balance in the almost constant company of mental specialists and asylum keepers.

The psychiatrists were very difficult, my informant states.

"There was one fat mental specialist with a queer glint in his eyes who kept on asking me if I heard voices. He meant when you hear voices and there aren't any. Well, I never heard voices. And if I did, I wouldn't have been mad enough to tell him. And every time I told him I didn't hear voices you should have seen the look of disappointment that came into his face. I had the uneasy feeling that he heard voices all day long, talking all kinds of blah to him, and why he wanted me to say I also heard those voices was so that he wouldn't feel so alone.

"I even got so, after a while, that I would sit for hours on end in my padded cell, just listening. I thought that if perhaps I could only hear one voice, just saying a few simple things to me, and I could repeat it to the psychiatrist, he would feel a lot better. But it just wouldn't work. During all the time that I was locked up in that madhouse I never once heard voices. And it wasn't from want of trying." Thus spoke a former inmate of a mental hospital who was discharged, I suppose, on the grounds that he was incurable.

Now, this whole question of insanity, officially classified as such, raises a number of interesting problems, some of them insoluble, except, possibly, by a lunatic.

There is Edgar Allan Poe's story of a man's visit to an insane asylum. The visitor is taken round by a person whom he believes to be the doctor in charge of the institution, but who eventually turns out to be the chief lunatic, for there had taken place, unknown to the outside world, a lunatic's revolution at this establishment, with the result that the lunatics had taken the places of the medical men and the keepers, these latter being now kept in confinement under the surveillance of their former charges.

It is a gripping story. It is a story that has got everything. But what puzzled me at the time I read it, was the question as to how this substitution of authority was ever detected. I mean, how is it possible ever to tell?

I feel that a change-over of this description has taken place in many of the world's best asylums before today (you know how cunning lunatics are) and with nobody the wiser.

When once a change of this nature has taken place in the administration, it seems only too simple to keep the new regime in power for ever. Picture yourself as the visitor to this institution. The new superintendent (former head lunatic) shows you around.

The first patient he will confront you with, as a matter of course, will be the former superintendent.

"A very interesting case, this one," the new superintendent will inform you. "It's all frightfully intricate. We have diagnosed it as dementia praecox with diurgic aberrations of the left cranial tissues. It's a species of insanity that is mystifying Krafft-Ebing and Walters and other psychiatrists and schizophrenics who are making a special study of it."

At this stage, of course, the former superintendent will announce his identity, which will be just what the new superintendent wants in order to establish his point.

"You're mad," the former superintendent will announce to the man who has usurped his job. "In fact," – and he will try to approach the visitor confidentially, lowering his voice and looking knowingly at him – "in fact, they are all mad, here. I am really the superintendent. The lunatics have taken charge of the place here and have locked me up. I am busy writing to the

Department of the Interior about it. You ought to see the copies I have got of all the letters I have written to the Department of the Interior. Stacks of letters and I get no answer. I am beginning to think that the Department of the Interior is also mad."

"Like I said to you," the new superintendent will announce to the visitor, "just about incorrigible. We give him all the pencils and paper he wants for writing. It takes his mind off things. But when once a man becomes graphomaniac, like he is, there isn't much hope for him."

You can go on this way ad lib. Because, in actual fact, you don't know where you are, in this world. It's a frightening thought. Take any book on psychopathology, written by almost any authority on abnormalities of the brain, either in its structure or its functions, and after a couple of paragraphs, if you know anything about the art of letters, you can feel to what an extent graphomania has been the dynamism that has impelled the author to sit down and write the book at all.

You will also discover, after the first couple of pages, that the writer is going to impart to you his own individual theories, which are completely different from any theories any other psychiatrist has ever held, and from then onwards the writer enters a realm of marvellously disconnected fantasy, where he can let himself go just as mad as he likes.

Something that I have also learnt from my ex-mental-hospital-inmate informant – and it is something that has shaken me – is the fact that the patients in mental institutions are no longer required to wear a distinctive garb. Now, in the old days, it was different. The custom of making the patient wear a uniform decorated with stripes or squares or daisy-chains was very sensible. It gave you a good rough and ready idea as to who was who in a lunatic asylum. But today that has gone by the board. The present-day situation is one fraught with peril. In the rough and tumble of trying to establish, under prevailing conditions, as to who is the mental specialist and who the mental case requiring treatment, some pretty ghastly scenes must get enacted. And the strain, of course, is on the keepers.

The whole field of insanity is of absorbing importance at the present time. To all of us. It is enough if you have got a fixed stare in your eyes and you seem sure of what you are doing, for people to be impressed with you and to invest you with all the qualities of leadership. Human nature can't take in the idea that a man should look as mad as all that, and carry on in a mad fashion, and on top of all that actually be mad. It doesn't seem logical.

You can see this happening everywhere, and not only in the sphere of statesmanship. Where a man with a one-track in-sanity type of mind comes along, normal people instinctively stand aside. They accord him all due respect straight away. They can't believe that a man can have all that insane energy, and still be wrong.

In this respect we are still very primitive. We stand in the same awe of energetic insanity as did any of the members of a primitive tribe. We are actually in a more dangerous position than are savages with their taboos and rigid caste systems – all aimed at keeping the lunatic out. We even go so far as to allow him to write treatises on psychopathology. This is a terrible thought.

As a result of all this, we civilised human beings are all caught up in a whirlpool of mental aberrations, our thoughts moulded in terms of chaos conceived by lunatics of both the past and the present. To take just a simple example. Almost every civilised person you come across will tell you that the earth isn't flat. It's round. It's like an orange. It is, to be still more technical, an oblate spheroid. And the authority he quotes for this is that some astronomer a few hundred years ago saw it all in a telescope. Copernicus, and he saw it all moving.

The point of all this, obviously enough, is that the earth is flat. And it doesn't move. These facts are so axiomatic that you don't even need to test them out for yourself. You have just got to look at the earth and see. And you can feel it doesn't move.

Our whole mental attitude towards life is hedged around with unrealities of this description. We live in a chaos of ideas thought out by cranks. We have been unable to protect our civilisation from the perilous invasion of the lunatic, whom we have been unable to keep out. The result today, when you reject insanity, and you depict things just as they are, and you see the sun as Phoebus, as Apollo, as Ra bestriding the heavens, and a red sky in the morning is the shepherd's warning, then it sounds as though you are trying to talk poetry. Whereas it is all just plain, factual stuff, based on simple observations and divest of insanity.

We all know the expression, "playing mad". In this mad world there are, alas, a good many of us who have to engage in the pastime of "playing sane". There is quite a lot of fun in it. Playing sane-sane.

The Disappearance of Latin

A few days ago, in the course of a conversation with a couple of people connected with education, I learnt, with sincere feelings of regret, that Latin is gradually disappearing from the curriculum of our South African schools. Latin is being replaced by other languages or by commercial subjects. And the scholars who take Latin for Matriculation are declining in number every year.

This is all wrong, somehow. Apart from its cultural value, the study of Latin is essential to the moulding of character.

Of course, a great deal of rubbish has been talked and written through the centuries about the value of various subjects in the school syllabus in the direction of developing moral virtues. When cardboard modelling was introduced in the primary school, for instance, it was claimed by its protagonists that cardboard modelling exercises an elevating influence on the young mind and that pupils who studied this subject for two hours a week would grow up into good and upright citizens.

The moral virtues you acquired through doing cardboard modelling included I believe, that of honesty, tenacity of purpose, spiritual concentration, a high idealism, determination and chastity. You also learnt physical courage, that way.

Woodwork was even better for building character, for developing the nobler qualities of mind and soul, the loftier attributes of the spirit.

The point is that cardboard modelling was tried out. And the children who studied cardboard modelling in the lower standards grew up into men and women who were not in any way noticeably better human beings than the previous generation of pupils who had not been privileged to practise the art of making things out of cardboard and gummed paper.

In spite of cardboard modelling, a whole generation of scholars went into the world and didn't cut life's cardboard straight. The real trouble with cardboard modelling is that it makes for cynicism at too tender an age: it teaches the child that life is all just lath and plaster – sawdust and cardboard.

But it's different with Latin.

If the present tendency in our system of education continues, Latin will, in the course of the next few years, have become a dead language. And this isn't right. For one thing, the interests of good-fellowship demand that we keep the ancients with us: as foreigners, maybe, but as foreigners with whose tongue we are tolerably familiar and whose accents do not fall jarringly on the modern ear. Unfamiliarity with the stranger's home language is one of the most potent causes of xenophobia. And we don't want the people who wrote the western – if less enchanting – half of classic literature to be excluded from our society merely because their language sounds uncouth and falls harshly on the polite ear.

I don't mean we have got to accept the whole literature. I can understand anybody drawing the line at Virgil: "Aut redit a nobis aurora diemque reducit", or "-tremens procumbit humi bos".

No, I feel that Virgil is a foreigner who will never really become assimilated. Not even his "Quidquid id est, timeo Danaos et dona ferentes", no matter how often it is quoted by high school headmasters, is quite free from that inelegance, that infelicity bordering on vulgarity, which we so mistakenly associate with the foreigner.

But then there is Cicero. There is also Horace. Above all, there is Ovid. No matter what Ovid is like on the outside, he has got an inner refinement that we cannot do without. He is quite unmistakably one of the boys of the game. We have just got to invite him to the party.

But apart from purely cultural considerations, there is another reason why our educational authorities must insist on Latin being retained in the curriculum. The study of Latin builds character. If you have Latin throughout your school years, and you have enough of it, you will never, in later life, become decadent – no matter how weak-willed you are naturally, or to what extent your blood-stream is tainted with the various forms of congenital depravity. And no matter how checkered your life may be, a thorough grounding in Latin during the formative years will pull you through every subsequent vicissitude.

The mental effort you have to put into acquiring a mastery of the rules of Latin grammar – prose, syntax, conjugations, declensions, "ut" with the subjunctive, the ablative absolute, indirect statement – all that can only make your mind four-square and imbue your nature with a purposeful earnestness and impart to your character a quality of granite that will remain inside of you, irrespective of what surface qualities of gaiety and apparent irresponsibility you acquire later on for purely decorative purposes.

The iron introduced into your soul through the weary hours of slogging away at Latin will remain.

That is where, when it comes to character-building Latin is so superior to mathematics. Mathematics teaches you to be slick, the use of ingenuity, to look for quick ways – saying a dozen times so many pennies are the same number of shillings, and using logarithm tables, instead of multiplying out. But there is no nonsense like that about Latin. There is only hard, honest toil. The result when you have studied Latin, is that in later life you approach an issue in an honest, stupid, straightforward fashion, which is the right way, in the long run, for approaching any issue. You don't look for loopholes. Evasions are all right for securing short-range results. Honest stupidity is the only thing that brings you lasting satisfaction – even if it is only for the reason that you are too stupid to know any better.

Penology and education being, for obvious reasons, closely interrelated sciences, it is as well to consider, for a moment, the advisability of introducing the study of Latin as a prison task for our convicts along with the more orthodox activities of packing oakum, sewing mail-bags and breaking stones. The compulsory study of Latin in prison could go a long way towards reforming our criminal classes. How the convicts will hate those dreary hours of drudgery! Hours spent in the hall with grammars and textbooks, under the supervision of broken-down and retired Latin teachers.

The compulsory study of Latin as a routine part of the hard labour course will lead to the reform of many otherwise incorrigible criminals. "The stone pile was nothing," I can imagine a reformed recidivist saying, "and I could always do solitary. But that fourth-year Latin class left me a broken man. I am only 52 – and look at me. O tempora, o mores."

No, Latin is not a dead language. There is a great future for it.

Spring!

Spring is y-cumen? This means a variety of things. The vines are beginning to put forth tendrils that in three months' time will be transformed into grapes purpling in the sunshine. The jacaranda and the kaffirboom will soon be in terrible flower. Lots more people will be patronising the swimming baths. In that area covered by indigenous thorn trees, just beyond the Observatory curve, that is known as Bezuidenhout's Farm and that is the Witwatersrand's last remaining link with the bushveld, myriads of white butterflies will be fluttering about the low scrub at the approach of the evening, and in the grass will be the drone of innumerable insects, and in the lengthening of the shadows there will be the strange fragrance of a new springtime, and with the nightfall the season's first Amalaita will saunter in through the west gate.

Above all, with the coming of a new spring, millions of gaudily-coloured thoughts will be bursting in the poet's brain.

And with the spring in our midst we feel that we should talk of God, not in the way the theologians do, but in a spirit of profound veneration. In other words, we should introduce God with a song and dance. We should be glad of Him.

We should dredge up out of our twentieth century Western Civilisation souls some of that antique joy that our forefathers knew when with maypole and wassail and saraband and heyday they welcomed the advent of another springtime. And also with whoopee and kiss in the ring. It is almost as though the world no longer believes in God.

The arrival of each spring makes itself known in a different way, and yet a different moment, to every one of us.

You are suddenly conscious of a deep inner thrill; your pulse seems to quicken for no reason; the air is filled with a slow beauty, and when you breathe it is with a sense of delight that recalls bygone, dolorous things, and the thoughts that surge into your head are wild . . . oh, wild . . . You know by these signs that spring is at hand.

And this awareness can come to you in the most unexpected places. When you have just boarded a tram-car, for instance, and the conductor is reiterating the old untruth about there being plenty of room upstairs; and you discover all at once that his story does not fall jarringly on your ear. Or you are in a crowded thoroughfare, and your imagination is captured by the sudden colour of the sun on a street-sign; and you know that romance is waiting around the corner with a cherry between her teeth.

Spring doesn't care how awkward the moment is that she chooses to tell you that she is here. She comes to a book-keeper sitting in front of a ledger, and a foolish smile comes over his face, and his pen remains poised in mid-air, and he doesn't see the figures on the page any more, but only a dark beckoning. Spring comes to a girl behind a milk-bar counter, and so when the customer goes out he also feels mixed up, somehow. Or spring comes to the blacksmith playing a tune on the anvil with his ball-pen hammer, and so his striker brings down his sledge onto the piece of iron at the wrong time, because unknown to himself the blacksmith has been beating out the rhythm of a light, gay ditty on the anvil; and so the blacksmith curses his striker for not bringing down the sledge at the right time; but all the while the blacksmith is thinking to himself that as soon as he gets home he will take off his jacket and roll up his sleeve and write a letter to his poor old grey-haired mother.

All such things does the spring do when she arrives.

But I like it best of all when the spring announces her presence on some evening – in the early part of it – in the dim lustre of the twilight and the pale smell of dusk. Her tread does not awaken the silence of the grass; it is almost as though the world stays hushed for her muted passage. But a little later, when the night wind stirs, you can feel the breath of the springtime in it. You know what is in the wind.

When I was young and I read comic papers I was always struck by the fact that once a year, round April somewhere, these English publications would carry humorous drawings about the spring. And a favourite subject for these illustrators was a green meadow with lambs gambolling on it, and the figure of a poet flinging his arms and legs about in a frisky curvetting. And the caption to this kind of comic drawing would invariably be "Spring".

Perhaps they still have these comics: I don't know: I haven't read them for so many years.

But I feel that this attitude towards the poet – the man-in-the street's attitude – is the right one. No matter what sort of genius, or lack of it, even, there may be in a poet's Ode to the Spring, the poet as a person must not be taken with heavy earnest. The comic conception of a poet, whether he is writing immortal tragedies in front of a flickering taper in an attic, or whether he is performing a springtime hop-skip-and-jump in a field, is the only kind of conception that rings true to me. It is an idea of a poet that has very old and very respected traditions. The idea of a poet as a minstrel, a singer, a scarecrow mountebank, a jongleur.

But it is all so different today. The poet has become such a solemn person. So heavy and ponderous, invested with such grave dignity. (But I should worry with the spring outside.)

Take the average Afrikaans poet today. Both in his self-conscious attitude towards himself as the creator of inspired verse and as somebody contributing to a nation's culture, and also in the reverential attitude towards him on the part of the public, there is none of that joy and gaiety – and warm, human comedy – that is awakened in the heart at the thought of a troubadour. Perhaps it is that our poets today haven't got it in them, any more, to be troubadours. Which is a pity. The result is that they become comic figures in another sense.

Myself, I don't take kindly to the idea of the poet becoming somebody pontifical. If this goes on much longer we shall shortly be taking our poets as seriously as we do our footballers. (But is that important, with spring in the air?)

The right attitude towards art of any kind is that we should be very jolly about it. Johannesburg had the right spirit in the old days.

A man told me about the time Paderewski came to play in the Wanderers' Hall. Johannesburg was then a mining camp and the citizens were pleased and flattered that a world-famous celebrity had come to honour them with a visit, and so they turned up in force, determined to give Paderewski the most rousing reception he had ever had. They passed a bottle of whisky on to the stage, so that he could have a swig before he started playing. And they enjoyed his music so much that they stamped their feet on the wooden boards in accompaniment to a Chopin prelude, and as Paderewski's fingers swept over the keyboard they shouted out their encouragement to him, and when they knew a few snatches of a melody, here and there, they sang "Tra-la-la-la," like that, with great gusto.

Anyway, Paderewski didn't give any more concerts in Johannesburg. Apparently he also held sacerdotal ideas about a pianist's status.

With the beginning of the spring all sorts of seeds are being sown. These – according to a gardening catalogue – include gladioli, beans, beets, cosmos, dahlias ("before planting, scatter a mixture of equal parts of soot, wood-ash and superphosphate over the bed, using two ounces of the mixture to every square yard of soil"), Brussels sprouts and sunflowers. I think it would be nice to plant them all together in one bed, with "such truly warm-weather subjects as tomatoes, mealies and string and Lima beans".

I also like the luscious sound of the names of the following bulbs: "Pink or white watsonias, lilies, ranunculi and anemones."

But the old sunflower takes a lot of beating.

The daffodil follows the sun. But the sunflower doesn't. Oh no. The sunflower is too proud for that.

The sunflower thinks he is also a sun. He hears people talk about him and call him a sunflower. And he knows he has got a big, fat yellow face. And so he thinks he is just like the sun, and that in daylight, if people pass near him, he makes them hot, just like the sun does. And this is true, of course. You have only to put your hand in front of the glowing face of a sunflower on a summer's day, and you will see how your hand gets warmed.

Actually, the sunflower thinks he is better than the sun; and when the sun shines right into his face, he jeers at the sun. "You," the sunflower says to the sun – just like that, in tones of mockery – "You, yes. Huh! Where's your stem?"

And so the spring has come into our midst, leading the gaudy procession of the seasons.

In the ice-cream factories the bicycle tyres are being inflated. In the prison the convicts are handing in their winter jerseys. In a classroom the young teacher, with her thoughts elsewhere, gets a wrong answer to the sum on the blackboard. In the mine compound an aged Xhosa nods his head in sage approval of the green-hued contents of a paraffin tin. In Eloff Street a traffic cop takes off his cap and with a low obeisance to a motorist – no, but this cannot happen, not even in the spring. And there, in this office, I am sweating on the top line to get this article finished, because the printer is waiting for the copy, tra-la. Tra-la-la.

Home Town

Last week I revisited Kuils River, a village that is a few miles outside of the Cape Town municipal area and that enjoys the questionable distinction of being the place in which I was born. How shall I describe my feelings on alighting at the shabby little railway station and gazing about me at my unfamiliar birthplace, which I saw again, now, for the first time since the age of four? I felt very lonely. There was nothing about the place I recognised. And if it wasn't for the fact that Table Mountain looked quite near – through its proximity at least giving me some sort of a clue as to whereabouts I was – I feel sure that I would have caught the next train back again. I felt so lost, both emotionally and geographically.

I had only one conscious memory of Kuils River. That was when I was about two. I was seated on the grass, wrapped around in a blanket and there was a soft wind blowing, because it was getting on towards sunset, and two young girl-cousins, a few years older than I, were dancing about me on the grass. And I suddenly burst into tears, just like that, without reason. And the sadness of that memory has, at intervals, haunted me throughout the rest of my life.

But as I strolled down a quiet little road in the direction of the village, with the station behind me, it suddenly struck me that while I remembered nothing at all of the external features of my birthplace, there was something else, something timeless and more vivid than memory, that made me intimately acquainted with my surroundings, even though I didn't know where the path on which I was walking, that lay deep in white dust, would lead to. In the stir of the noonday breeze was something anciently familiar. And the patches of bluish-coloured grass, sifted around with dune sand: were these not the things I had always known? And a sudden fragrance, coming off from the warm earth and blending with the subtle odour of black-wattle bark, overwhelmed me for a moment, almost, as though I had left Kuils River only yesterday.

Far from requiring Table Mountain any longer as a comforting landmark, I now began to feel that I could show other people the way around, here in this village. Even though I had to enquire of passing strangers the way to the main street, where the village stores were, and the post office, and the local pub.

And because life in Kuils River is very leisurely, with the pace of things smooth and unhurried, I found many people who were glad to hold converse with a visitor from Johannesburg, and they told me many things, and at great length, about my home town from which I had emigrated at the age of four. And from numerous enquiries I made, putting my questions judiciously and in all sorts of roundabout ways, I elicited the fact that nobody in Kuils River had ever heard of me.

At least, the first lot of enquiries I made were of a tentative nature. I would ask, clearing my throat somewhat self-consciously, whether Kuils River did not perhaps have a few literary traditions, kind of; whether there was any local knowledge of anybody, distinguished, sort of, having been in Kuils River during the present century, sort of – in the literary line like? All sorts of diffident, indirect questions like that. That was how I started off. But afterwards I just began asking them straight out. And the replies were always, monotonously, the same. There was Dr. F. C. L. Bosman, they said, of Cape Town University. Well, he was a writer, of course. And he was born in Kuils River. And C. H. Kuhn ("Mikro"), the author of the Afrikaans bestseller *Toiings*, had come to settle in Kuils River some years ago, to write, and everybody in the village was very proud to have him there, of course. And it was well known that the local dominie had been contributing morally uplifting stories to the Afrikaans religious press for a good number of years. That was the sum total of Kuils River's literary associations, but for a small place like that it wasn't at all bad, they said.

"No, it isn't at all bad," I agreed, each time.

Taken all round, it seemed to me that there could be such a

thing, in Kuils River, as overdoing the old truth about a prophet not being without honour.

I enquired, later in the afternoon, as to whether there were any historical monuments in Kuils River – any ancient, time-worn edifices, any noble and inspiring ruins. And they said yes, there was. They said there was Colonel Creswell. They said he lived at the top end of Kuils River, on an estate barricaded with palisades and with savage dogs roaming the grounds. They said that several English families had settled in Kuils River and that they all went in for tall stake-fences and fierce mastiffs.

I dashed off in the direction of where they indicated to me Colonel Creswell's house was, after they had again cautioned me about the Hounds of the Baskervilles loping about the wooded grounds with slavering jaws. Colonel Creswell. I couldn't believe it. What volumes of water had not flowed under Vaal River bridge, in dry seasons and all, since I had last seen Colonel Creswell's name in a newspaper.

I found the place, huge, rambling, closed in with pointed poles like what Harold's army erected before Hastings. I located the gate with some difficulty. It was a good distance up the driveway to the house, and I had to kick a big dog out of the way that was lying asleep in the sun. He disappeared into the undergrowth with a yelp. I was still considerably out of breath when, having been admitted by a servant into the drawing-room, I sat down to wait for Colonel Creswell to appear.

But I was glad I had come. I stayed there all afternoon. Towards evening we went and sat on the stoep. In appearance Colonel Creswell was more like the cartoons of him that had appeared in anti-Pact newspapers in those far-off days than he resembled a studio photograph of himself in the drawing-room. But that was all the years had done to him. His mind was as bright as ever. He was a fund of enthralling reminiscences. Intimate little stories about Merriman and Botha and Hertzog. And when he said that Smuts had never forgiven him he wiped his left eye, which was watering. He spoke about his birthplace, Malta or Gibraltar – I forget which he said – and about the first mine he worked on on the Rand, the Durban-

Roodepoort, and about his having had to sever his connection with the Chamber of Mines in rather a big way, on account of some Chinamen he had kicked out.

"Don't you go back to the Rand sometimes?" I asked, "to go and have a look at the Durban-Roodepoort again, for instance – all the old scenes?"

But Colonel Creswell said that he was already 85, and that while he would like to visit the Rand some day, there was hardly anybody there that still knew him. So he preferred Kuils River. It seemed very sad, somehow. And so I told Colonel Creswell – and he was the only person in the village in whom I had confided this fact – that I was born in Kuils River – and that there was not a soul in my birthplace that knew me. We sat for a good while after that in silence.

The wind of early evening, sweeping across from the dunes, stirred through the tangled undergrowth. And it seemed chillier than the wind that blew from over the dunes when I was a child.

Cape Town Castle

We walked through the imposing entrance to the Cape Town Castle surmounted by the curved arms of the chief citizen of Holland and the V.O.C. monogram of the Dutch East India Company, and we were studying the patterns engraved on the seventeenth century cannons that are planted in the ground thereabouts, with their muzzles pointed skywards, when a guide came and took charge of us.

In Western Europe I had got into the habit, after a while, of running whenever anybody resembling a professional guide approached me. I had found that guides were, in general, ignorant men, devoted to the obvious and the sensational and with little understanding of the fact that when I was in a strange city I had no desire to be shown churches and squares and museums and historical sites included in Cook's tour itinerary.

I remember an occasion on which a Flemish guide in Ostend conducted me to a colossal piece of statuary near the waterfront. It was a representation in black stone of a family of Congo Negroes delightedly lifting up their arms from which pended lengths of snapped fetters. Pieces of broken chains hung from their necks and ankles, also. The monument was erected, according to the inscription, as a memorial to King Leopold of the Belgiums.

I told the guide that it was an impressive monument and that I gathered from it that the seaport of Ostend had at one time been prominent in the slave trade. But the guide said it was a memorial to commemorate King Leopold's work in freeing the natives of the Congo.

As a result of the foregoing, when I had got into the forecourt of the *Cape Town Castle*, and what was obviously a professional guide began to approach our party, I made a half-turn to run. From force of habit. But then I remembered the sentry. And then I realised, for the first time, why the entrance to the main gateway of the Castle is guarded during visiting hours. So that a visitor can't run away from the guide.

We learnt that the Castle was commenced twelve years after Van Riebeeck's landing and that the present gateway had been opened by Simon van der Stel in 1662, the original entrance having faced the sea, which at that time apparently came a great deal nearer the Castle than it does today.

An interesting feature of the Castle is the Kat, or curtain, a cross-wall about 2 yards in length and 40 feet in height and 10 feet thick, which was erected by the original builders as an afterthought, in order to divide the courtyard into two halves for additional safety.

I took particular note of the woodwork, observing that the doorframes and rafters and other timbering were mostly of teak. There was no yellowwood. Here and there, the guide informed me, oak took the place of teak, which was all imported from the East. I was struck by the fact that in this, the oldest Cape Structure extant – on which building operations had continued until the latter part of the seventeenth century – no indigenous timber had been employed. I found that this circumstance was a strong argument in support of my theory that some of the old Cape Town houses, whose gables are undated and which are claimed to have been erected before the close of the year 1600, must actually have been built at a considerably later period.

Yellowwood is not indigenous to the Western Province: it has had to be imported from Knysna, several hundred miles from Cape Town. There is no teak timbering in any of the Cape houses I have visited – only yellowwood. These houses could therefore have been erected only at dates subsequent to the establishment of regular trade with Knysna, and it is obvious that no shipments of Knysna timber contributed to the building of the Castle. I discussed this matter with Mr. Thesen, whose family has been intimately associated with the Knysna timber industry for a good many generations, and he says that the tradition in the trade is that yellowwood and other timber was being imported into the Cape from Knysna at an early period in the history of European colonisation.

Anyway, the guide at the Castle was openly contemptuous when I mentioned yellowwood. The Castle was built of teak that had been carried in the holds of Dutch East Indiamen from Burma and Ceylon: by comparison, yellowwood seemed to him almost as new as the Rand.

Everything about the Castle made a most profound impression on me. Each brick seemed haunted with the atmosphere of the past. I was thrilled to learn that the lime used in the mortar was processed from the sea-shells that the builders' labourers collected on Robben Island. The stone steps on which our footsteps echoed were charged with historical associations. We saw the council chamber where the governor and his officers sat. And the bastions of Katzenellenbogen, Orange and Nassau. And the turret bell. And the balcony floored with blue tiles.

We passed through a heavy door and entered what looked at first like a prison cell, because it was a small, dark room, windowless and thick-walled. But when we looked down we saw that we were separated by a stone parapet from a well, which is described as being "situated below the centre archway and thus marked on the earliest seventeenth century plan of the Castle."

The pulley is still there, in position above the well. The last strands of the old frayed rope disappeared a little while ago, snatched by curio-hunters. In any case, they don't bother to fetch up water from the well today, and the pulley hasn't creaked on its axle for a long time, now. The water in the well is a good way down and it is covered with an oily film. Paraffin, the guide said, for the mosquitoes.

The next place we went into really was a prison cell. And when I saw the real thing, in seventeenth century terms, I understood why, when I had asked the guide if the well aperture was a place of incarceration, he had dismissed my query with a light laugh.

The dominant emotion I had, when the guide conducted us into the old prison cells, opening out from the end of a long, winding, airless underground passage, was that in the seventeenth century they had stronger and doughtier and stouter-hearted men than what we could produce today. I was satisfied that not the most hardened recidivist in South Africa's prison population at the present day would be able to do time in a place like that. It was just plain prison and no argument.

How can I describe one of those cells?

First let me try and explain how dark it is. The guide closed the door. We were inside. The recently-installed electric light was switched on. The guide bade us observe the white collar worn by a member of our party. Then he switched off the light. We were in darkness blacker than anything I have ever seen. Naturally, I could see nothing of the white collar in question, but I reached out my hand in the dark to touch it. It felt black.

The guide switched on the light once more. We felt relieved. I began to wonder if any of the prisoners who had been in that cell in the seventeenth century had worn white collars, and if they had tried a couple of tricks like that also. It was actually even a lot darker in the old days, the guide explained. Because then they had three doors, one behind the other, to close up the cell properly. And each door was sealed, literally, with strips of leather.

With the light on, we could see why the occupant of the cell didn't get suffocated in there a good while before his trial came off. In the arched ceiling was a dark hole, a couple of inches square, which turned and twisted – to prevent the penetration of even the murkiest gleams – through twenty feet of stone and brick to communicate with the outside air on top of the rampart.

I felt that if I had been a prisoner in that cell I wouldn't have worried about the dark so much. I would have been in terror that the warder, on the rampart, through carelessness or spite, would have put his foot on the air-hole.

That pitifully inadequate bit of ventilation, a small black hole spiralling and twisting upwards through twenty feet of masonry, made so deep an impression on me that I could not shudder at any further revelations made by the guide.

I was unmoved when he indicated how high the slime-

83

covered water had stood in the dungeon, making it difficult for the prisoner to sleep on the floor with any degree of real comfort. Or when he pointed to a part of the wall where the bricks were blackened from the smoky films of the seventeenth century candles, and he said that the official torturer used to set his candle down on that spot when he came in to adjust the thumb-screws; and that the candle had not been provided (as I at first thought) as a light for the prisoner to read a good book by.

And, of course, Adam Tas, whose life and personality are so intimately woven into the historical fabric of the Cape of two hundred and fifty years ago, comes into the picture here, too.

Adam Tas was imprisoned in the Castle by Wilhelm Adrian van der Stel for fourteen months.

In the Koopmans-de Wet Museum is a document bearing Adam Tas's signature. It is a magnificent signature, and he wrote it down before he went to gaol. I made a copy of Adam Tas's signature on that document, so impressed was I with its attitudinising flamboyance, with gorgeous ostentation of scroll and flourish. The way he wrote his name was like a parade marching past with trumpets. I can imagine Governor Adrian van der Stel saying to himself, when the trouble first started, that he would take at least two flourishes out of that signature before he had finished with Adam Tas. And I am sure that he succeeded, too.

I feel that when Adam Tas came out of that dungeon under the Katzenellenbogen bastion of Cape Town Castle, after fourteen months incarceration, he wrote his name, simply, "a tas".

Climbing Table Mountain

There are a number of things that I have been wanting to do in Cape Town, and since I have not succeeded in accomplishing them I have, as a result, been overtaken by a singular sense of frustration.

For one thing, I have been wanting to climb Table Mountain. Consequently we set off, in a party of three, early one morning, in hiking shorts, and went by bus to Kloof Nek, where – we were informed – a footpath winds all the way round the back of the mountain to the Blinkwater Gorge, up which you climb to the summit. The bus was crowded, and so we had to go and sit on top. I hoped that the road up Table Mountain would not be equally crowded. I made the ascent to the upper deck of the bus with comparative ease. The first part of the climb wasn't so bad, I said to myself. The bus came to a halt at the Kloof Nek terminus and we alighted without incident.

It was very pleasant sauntering along the footpath that winds around the lower slopes of Table Mountain. Stately pines towered above us, their fragrance wakening a haunting nostalgia, their nearness affording me a subtle sense of comfort. I felt that a tree trunk would be something substantial to hold on to, higher up the trail, should a sudden eventuality arise. But after a while I noticed that the pines were getting spaced out more and more. In the end, they gave out altogether. I looked up. For the rest of the way to the summit there seemed only rocks and krantzes.

I could sense that the other two members of our little party shared this feeling of uneasiness at the thought of our having now climbed out above the pine belt. There was about it a finality that seemed almost like that of doom. But we didn't let on to each other what we really thought. We only said that we were glad that there were no more pines around to obscure the view. We also said that if we got no higher up the mountain than we were now – which was, of course, absurd – it would have been well worth it, just for the magnificent prospect that met our gaze when we sat down by the footpath, after we had passed the last of the trees.

Below us lay Camps Bay. The oblong area of grasslands fronting the sea was reduced to the size of a good-class magazine. Far out at sea, where the blue of sky and ocean blended, we discerned a full-rigged ship which we recognised immediately, by her broad square stern and old-fashioned mizzensails, as the *Flying Dutchman* (captain, Mr. Van der Decken). We felt highly privileged at being able to view, even across so great a distance, that ancient Dutch East Indiaman, long celebrated in legend and song. We watched the ship until she disappeared below the horizon. Once again, in the course of two centuries of beating off the Cape of Storms, Van der Decken had failed to make the harbour. We had sort of imagined that he would fail.

We proceeded on our way. After a while we reached a signpost pointing silently and steeply upwards. It read: "Blinkwater Ravine – Blinkwater Kloof." In neither official language did that precipitous piece of direction sound particularly heartening. But that, clearly, was the way we had to go. Very reluctantly we left our well-trodden little footpath and started scrambling over rocks and shrubbery, onwards and upwards, following the way the signpost pointed. We were no longer skirting the lower slopes of the Lion's Rump. We were climbing Table Mountain in earnest. We thrilled to this knowledge. It was very exciting. At the same time – speaking strictly for myself, personally – I was conscious of a certain measure of trepidation.

The mountain towered in vast bulk above us. Below was a steep and empty desolation. The green of Camps Bay had dwindled to the size of a postage stamp. Van der Decken's ship was no longer there to cheer us up.

But we didn't let on to each other what we really felt.

It was getting on well towards midday, when, keeping as much to the left as we could, we found ourselves very high up and right inside the shadows of the kloof. It was chilly and we shivered. In whichever direction we looked, we saw the world bathed in brilliant sunshine. We alone, clambering upwards towards the top of the gorge, were in deep shadow. This thought made us shiver still more.

We could see that we had climbed a very long way, and we were very pleased with the effort we had made. The green of Camps Bay had disappeared altogether, but in front of us there stretched, extending into the infinite distance, an expanse of sea and sky and burning coastline that must remain as one of the most majestic sights on which it is possible for the gaze of man to rest. We could see clear out beyond Hout Bay and Slangkop to that lonely spot in the world where the Atlantic and Indian Oceans meet. Even to the untrained eye the line of demarcation between these two giant oceans is easily discernible. It is a thick straight line that looks as though it was drawn with a ruler. The Atlantic Ocean, on one side of this line, has got more of a cobalt tinge in its waters, while the Indian Ocean, on the other side of it, is more wavy, sort of. I don't know how deep down that line goes, but it must be a good number of fathoms, by the look of it.

After we had rested on that dizzy ledge for a while we embarked, by common accord and without any one of us having to make the suggestion, on the descent of Table Mountain. Getting down was easy. We sat well back and used our hands and feet only as brakes on our progress, when we appeared to be making the descent too quickly, and in order to circumvent jagged rock faces. But we adhered to our policy of resting at intervals. And on at least three occasions we had the satisfaction of being able to call out useful instructions to parties of climbers who passed near us on their way up. We were in high good spirits and did not admit – certainly not to each other – that we had turned back before we had reached the summit of Table Mountain. By the late afternoon we had got so far down the mountain-side that the green oblong of Camps Bay was again of substantial size, and when we caught another glimpse, in the westering sun, of Van der Decken's *Flying Dutchman*, coming back again over the horizon and with all sails set for Table Bay, we could have laughed to kill ourselves. We just knew he wouldn't make it.

Quite a number of people passed us that afternoon, all of them on their way up, along Blinkwater Gorge, to the top of Table Mountain. One of them was a woman pushing a pram.

Wreck and Roeland Street

I have been in Cape Town now for several months, and as a result of this sojourn I have discovered that in some respects Johannesburg is, in actual fact, a thousand miles away, and that in other respects the distance isn't so great.

When an Arabian Nights man, travelling non-stop by magic carpet, got from Baghdad to Peking in about the same length of time that it takes by aeroplane today, he didn't have any illusions about Peking having been brought any nearer to Baghdad by this speedier method of transport. He just had to look at all the Chinamen around him to realise from what a great distance he had really come. Indeed, as this particular story of the Thousand and One subsequently makes clear, the Arabian Nights man was shortly to regret the fact that Peking and all those Chinamen were not still further away from Baghdad.

And in regard to the distance between Johannesburg and Cape Town, two sets of circumstances have forced themselves on my attention: one was the shipwreck of the Greek ship, the *George M. Livanos*; the other is the projected demolition of the Roeland Street Gaol.

As far as the wreck of the *George M. Livanos* is concerned, I should like to say that it was a very dull affair. I have on occasion been shipwrecked much worse than that in Johannesburg. People said that a Greek ship had split in two halves on a rock just off Green Point. And so I started thinking of the Argonauts and the Golden Fleece and the face that had launched a thousand ships. Consequently I was more than a little disappointed when, arriving on the scene, I discovered that the *George M. Livanos* was not a trireme, but an ordinary tramp steamer, without much paint on her, and holed amidships, with one half finding a resting-place on the Green Point rocks and the other half settling comfortably into the Atlantic. The captain and the crew had abandoned the little ship quite a while before: being Greek, they were not only excellent sea-men, but were also endowed with a good deal of sound common sense.

They could take a hint from Poseidon as quick as anybody.

Nevertheless, when I repaired to the Green Point beach again, some days later, and I saw that the two halves of the ship had become still further sundered (so that the *George M. Livanos* would not float again, no, not this side of the Greek kalends), I realised that it had not been quite so colourless a shipwreck, after all. For down in her holds the *George M.* had had thousands upon thousands of bales of Australian wool. And with the battering of the blue waves of the Atlantic these bales had broken loose from the holds and had floated out into the ocean, bursting from the hessian bonds, and as far as the eye could see the spume of the billows bore on their white crests – curling in unblemished purity, the waves of the sea and the waves in the lambs' hair – the product of the last Australian wool clip.

Sly dogs, those Argonauts: in the unlighted holds of the *George M. Livanos* they had brought along the Golden Fleece, after all.

For an appreciable time after that, masses of Australian wool churned about in the sea from Green Point to beyond Camps Bay, tangling around the rocks like a new kind of white sea-weed, getting enmeshed in Neptune-Poseidon's trident every time he came up to have a look.

And I remember, on a subsequent public holiday, when I formed one of a long queue on Hout Bay beach that was waiting for the bus back to town, how intrigued I was at the action of a coloured woman who was standing at the far end of the line, with the sea up to her ankles because the queue was so long. A wind sprang up, whipping the fine beach sand against her bare legs; she stooped down and, nonchalantly lifting a quantity of lamb's combings out of the water, encased her legs in this protective covering. Well, we all know that wool keeps out the wind. And she did it all in a single movement, in which there was a kind of primitive poetry – almost as though she knew that what she had picked up out of the sea was part of the Golden Fleece.

The other circumstance that struck me in connection with the difference between Cape Town and Johannesburg relates to all the talk that is going on locally about the projected closing down of the Roeland Street Gaol. I am, naturally, not acquainted with Roeland Street Gaol: I am a Johannesburg man. But it would appear that this far-famed Cape Town prison has got just as much character, individuality, squalor, disagreeableness and romance as, say, the Johannesburg Fort. Now, it is when one placed the Fort in juxtaposition to Roeland Street that it would seem (to the person inside trying to look out) that Cape Town is not, after all, a thousand miles from Johannesburg. Indeed, I would imagine that if the Arabian Nights man sat himself down cross-legged on his magic carpet, in the awaiting trial yard of the Johannesburg Fort, and the magic carpet whisked him straight away into the hard labour section of Roeland Street Gaol – well, one couldn't really cavil at it if the Arabian Nights man felt that his carpet wasn't very magical, all of a sudden, and that it hadn't brought him such a very long distance . . .

Incidentally, it would be interesting to know why it is that certain prisons have developed a definite individuality, so that the sound of their names means something: Dartmoor, Sing-Sing, Alcatraz, San Quentin, the Breakwater. About these names there is a solid and eminently satisfactory grimness. Whereas, the names of lots of other prisons – and the world is full of prisons – evoke, by comparison, hardly any kind of emotional response.

Next to Roeland Street and The Fort, Pretoria Prison sounds colourless and insipid, almost just like being outside. And I wonder why that is. After all, has the Pretoria Gaol not got just as thick walls and just as heavy bars and just as small window apertures? – and are the warders not just as brutal and burly and the convicts as debased and sullen and hang-dog looking as their fellows in Roeland Street? And yet look at the difference in the sound of these two gaols in respect of tone, shuddery reaction and general showiness.

Anyway, I think it is a pity that prisons with so much individuality and tradition as The Fort and Roeland Street must go. But the authorities will no doubt try and replace them with gaols just as good. (And succeed.)

For the important things in life should not be dull. For those that go down to the sea in ships, and those that go to the local lock-up in leg-irons, a wreck should be like the *Waratah* or the *Hesperus* and not like the *George M. Livanos*: a pinch should mean Roeland Street or The Fort, and not Pretoria. Glug-glug . . . Clank.

The Cape Revisited

I was born in the Cape, in the Western Province. I have often been back there on visits. And it is singular that only on this last occasion, when I went to look again on holiday scenes, did I awaken to the fascination of the comparatively small area of the Union that lies between Table Mountain and the Hex River.

Because there is the Karroo, with its unyielding magnificence of grassless arid earth. Its silent majesty and breathless beauty, an allure that is irresistible because it is not on the surface; a stony beauty which is apparently easy to overlook because it is not obvious.

The Karroo has got none of the superficial grace of soft, easy curves and gentle verdancies. When the Karroo lays hold of you, therefore, you are bound by a spell that remains for ever. And there is the Free State. And there is the Transvaal Highveld. "Sing, o barren . . ." About the vlakte there is no spirit of a wanton invitingness. But there is a clinging bitterness and a straight-browed austerity; a stony, sterile bosom that holds out no beguilement. And when the message of these harsh places of the earth has got into your blood, and the mystery of things come to you unrefined, and not wrought into a pattern, then it is only with an effort, and at first but reluctantly, that you can bring your soul to an acceptance of beauty that has got resilience in it. (It is no doubt for this reason that Calvinism took root so readily among the Afrikaners of the Transvaal and the Free State. The Cape was too easy-going: and there were too many vine-clad hills and curved gables.)

And so because I had, by way of mistaken intolerance (as all intolerance is mistaken), come to affect a form of contempt for the Cape, on the score of its charms being flat and on the surface, I had to undergo the somewhat humiliating experience of learning that there was nothing new in my getting lyrical about what I came across there; and that people had in fact been rhapsodising about the Cape for years. I had to make the discovery that not only were the things that fascinated me all old things, but that my reactions to them were equally old.

Climatically this area, with its winter rains, is different from that of the rest of the southern Africa, and approximates to the climates surrounding the Mediterranean.

The small, fertile, mountainous area of the southern Cape, with its history of three hundred years of European settlement, is of unending fascination to anybody interested, romantically and culturally, in a country's past.

Many of the old farmhouses, built two centuries ago, are still standing, with their thatched roofs (which have to be renewed every few years) and their whitewashed walls – three foot thick, most of them – and their oak rafters and yellow-wood floors and ceilings, and their wine cellars and barns and out-houses, and their heavy doors and shutters that move creakily on ancient iron hinges that were forged by hand on the black-smith's anvil.

What captured my imagination about these old houses were, as much as anything else, the solid, cumbersome iron hinges, bitten into with the rust of centuries. They are not the bolt-hinges with which doors are hung today, or our fragile-looking modern T-hinges, but long, broad pieces of wrought iron, up to three-quarters of an inch in thickness, the sides curved and patterned in accordance with the craftsman's fancy, and made to pivot on a formidable staple thrust deep into the woodwork and wall.

Whenever I visit an old Cape house the first thing that takes my interest is the style and shape of the gable. After that I begin to study the style and design of the hinges on the doors, the rusted nails of two and a half centuries ago with their square, broad heads and the bolts that were not secured, as today, by a nut turned into a thread, but were hammered red-hot through the yellowwood door, to be riveted on to the hinge hole on the other side.

I have not said much about that other – possibly the most striking – characteristic of old Dutch architecture of the Cape, the wide gable rising in low flexures over the top of the wall, curling in leisurely convolutions against and above the dark thatch, much in the way that the big white clouds float curved over the summits of Hottentot's Holland mountains. The curved gable is an inevitable and intrinsic part – not of decoration but a homespun necessity of any thatched building in a southern Cape valley.

The circumstances surrounding the historical trouble between Governor Wilhelm Adrian van der Stel and Adam Tas seemed so intricately threaded through the early days of Dutch and Huguenot settlement at the Cape: so many legends are still current about it, so many relics of it remain, scattered over the Western Province, as though flung there by the violence of the administrative explosion which resulted in a governor getting sacked and a large number of colonists going to prison; there are so many remembrances of the affair extant in the form of documents and pieces of furniture and the outside walls of houses and in the living shape of oaks and pines and camphorwood trees, that I was under the necessity, right at the start, of looking up the episode again in a school history book.

I can still remember as a child (in standard two, I think it was), at about the fifth lesson in South African history, when the teacher got to Adrian van der Stel.

No doubt the story made an equally painful impression on the minds of other scholars. Because everything at the Cape had been going so smoothly until then. The landing of Jan van Riebeeck and the founding of the colony for the purpose of provisioning ships sailing between Europe and the East. Everything was so respectable. Idealistic, even. Jan van Riebeeck was a good man. And then Simon van der Stel, who founded Stellenbosch. A good man, too. He planted oak trees and completed the Castle started by Jan van Riebeeck to keep out the Hottentots. A good man and a fine governor. And then it was announced that the next governor was Adrian van der Stel. The child mind, eager to learn even nobler things about him than his predecessor, suffered the disillusionment that the next governor at the Cape was a crook.

It was a pleasant morning in the late summer that we set off on a four-mile stroll through leafy avenues in quest of the farm *Vergelegen*, where Adrian van der Stel had built his mansion and had set a thousand slaves to till the soil two and a half centuries ago.

Ambling through the lanes through this valley in the Hottentot's Holland, cool with the shade of old pines and oaks, we had no difficulty in finding our way to *Vergelegen*. Where we were in doubt we addressed ourselves to passers-by. Our questions were always the same.

"Is this the road to the place where that scoundrel Adrian van der Stel stayed?" we would enquire.

And we would be assured that we were going the right way. The form that our question took occasioned no surprise. Sometimes, for the word "scoundrel" we would subsitute "embezzler", or "thief", or, more simply "cad". And the response, made with hardly so much as the raising of an eyebrow, would always be the same. Yes, we were on the right road.

In so natural a manner did they answer our two-hundred-and-fifty-year-old questions about *Vergelegen* that it was almost as though Adrian van der Stel was still dishing out placaats from there.

About four miles from the village of Somerset West, on a tree by the side of the road, was a board bearing the name "*Vergelegen*". We passed through a gate and within a few minutes found ourselves on a path thickly shaded by oaks of immense girth: old trunks, gnarled and twisted and hollowed and contemporaneous in appearance, almost, with the oaks that grew until a few years ago in the Cape Town gardens and whose planting was ascribed to the time of Simon van der Stel. I could readily believe that the oaks forming the avenue to the *Vergelegen* Homestead had been planted by Simon van der Stel's son, Adrian.

Some distance down the avenue, where the foliage seemed specially dense, we sat down by the roadside and lunched off sandwiches and beer. I cast about – and discovered without much difficulty – a hollow oak to sit down in. The day was silent; the thick leafage sheltered us from the heat of high noon; no wind stirred the dappled pattern of shadow and light spread at our feet; our minds were at peace; in our thinking was the calmness of the moss on the oak trees' hollow bole.

For a while we rested there, watching the smoke from our cigarettes rising in slow spirals through the placid air, interested only in the smoke wreaths that were like frail ghosts haunting and getting lost in the green ceiling that the oaks had erected above us. And such was the feeling of time long passed away that was borne in upon us in the avenue laid out by Adrian van der Stel, that it seemed to me that the three of us seated at the foot of that ancient oak were phantoms also, palely loitering by the side of the seventeenth and eighteenth centuries.

Vergelegen was the first of the old Cape houses that we were to visit. And as we sojourned by the roadside, it was almost as though we sensed that it was meet that we should tarry there awhile, waiting without the portals, because when we crossed the threshold it would not be that of *Vergelegen* only: our feet would carry us over the wider doorstep. We would be entering a region that was separated from Johannesburg not merely by a thousand miles, but by a quarter of a millenium. We would be passing through a lintel in which, like in the dust of the road beside which we were seated, there was imprisoned the sunshine and the shadow and the fragrance of two and a half centuries.

I should like to say, right at the start, that as regards the main features of the place, the house itself, I was fated to be disappointed in *Vergelegen*. I was expecting to find the house that had been built on that farm, at the close of the seventeenth century, by Wilhelm Adrian van der Stel. (I hadn't read Theal then, and so I was ignorant of the Dutch East India Company's instructions for the demolition of Adrian van der Stel's home. The instructions were very detailed, too, even going to the extent of specifying as to what had to be done with the timber salvaged from the ruins.)

The homestead at *Vergelegen* is surrounded by an old wall

that I liked. In front of the house are a number of magnificent camphorwood trees. I believe implicity that they were planted in 1666. They ware grand, stately things. If somebody were to tell me that Vasco da Gama, through some whim, went and planted those camphorwood trees in the Hottentot's Holland valley two hundred years before Adrian van der Stel got there, I would believe that, also. It is difficult, without going into unseemly raptures, to convey something of the impression that those trees make on the visitor's mind. Perhaps the Dutch East India Company didn't notice those camphorwood trees, growing on the other side of the wall. Obviously, they neglected to give instructions for the trees to be chopped down.

The trouble with the farmhouse (the main building) on *Vergelegen* is that it doesn't give you an impression of age, somehow: in the same way that when you see an antique in a museum it is difficult to get the right feeling about. There is little about the building itself that can give one even an approximate idea of the time it was erected. We know that the original house was demolished in 1707. So the present building must have come after that. And I should imagine that it was a good while after. So much of it was restored in the early years of the present century, when the property was owned by Sir Lionel Philips, that I was not afforded much of a thrill in going over the house.

The woodwork was all so very new, for instance. (The door and the window frames and the wood and glass screen separating the lounge from the voorkamer are acknowledged as belonging to the present century.)

I was similarly disappointed in the yellowwood flooring. The boards were of the regulation width and thickness. But they weren't worn. And the beams were perfectly straight and square. Now I have got a fondness for old beams. In England I saw a good number of Elizabethan houses in which the oaken rafters had obviously been renewed somewhere in the nineteenth century. But I also saw Elizabethan houses where I was left in no doubt as to the antiquity of the blackened timbers, and there was much in contemporary England, including the decadence of present-day English drawing-room comedy, that I could forgive in the moment of contemplating the things that

Time had done to woodwork that had been installed when Shakespeare was still busy writing.

Such an Elizabethan house is the Roebuck Inn, a couple of miles into Sussex, on the main road to Lewes. The proprietor told me that the inn had been the resort of eighteenth century smugglers, a circumstance that was of small moment to me, smuggling seeming to be an affair only of yesterday, whereas the hand that had laid the axe to that age-blackened beam had been dust for close on four hundred years.

Similarly, whenever I visit an old farmhouse in the Cape, and a man or a woman, to create the "atmosphere" of the past, said that such and such was a slave bell tower, or that some whitewashed dwelling had once housed slaves, I was not impressed. We owned slaves in the Cape until yesterday. If they could show me nothing older than that, they would be wasting my time.

If the house that is now standing on *Vergelegen* had been inspected by the Dutch East India Company, they would not have bothered to tear it down.

But there is an old wine-cellar immediately behind the main building. That long wine-cellar, with its low, whitewashed walls and its enormous black door is unforgettable. I would not mind going many miles out of my way to revisit it.

I was told that in the early years of the century, when a number of alterations were being made to the place, the workmen at *Vergelegen* unearthed a lot of foundations. I should imagine that those foudations date back to the original building erected by Adrian van der Stel. There is also a very old decaying wall some little distance removed from the site of the present farmhouse. It is a thick wall constructed of very small bricks that you can't prise out of the mortar even today. I know, because I tried.

I stood before the battered relic, that venerable and discoloured ruin, and I felt that the shapeless pile of masonry, about twelve feet high and perhaps twenty yards long and over three feet in thickness, was all that remained of the palatial mansion that Adrian van der Stel had built in the palmy days of the East India Company. That weather-beaten structure, green with age, a piece of wall that, standing alone, seemed a formless decapitation, had nevertheless survived the hands of the East India Company's demolition gang and the wind and rain of two and a half centuries. So my feelings, when I stood by that wall, were of awe. That weed-garmented reminder of the past evoked in me a reverence which I feel I would not have known in the roomy halls of old *Vergelegen* long ago, when Adrian van der Stel's star was still in the ascendant, and before Adam Tas got to work on him.

You can only know a University if you have attended classes in it as a student. Otherwise you can only prowl around it as a visitor, and that, of course, doesn't count.

I have frequently prowled around Oxford as a visitor, but I was not able to gather much about the place except that it was conveniently situated in fairly close proximity to Morris-Cowley's motor works. I thought that this was rather useful, because if an apprentice to the motor industry found that the task of turning out brass screws of various intricate dimensions on a lathe was beyond the range of his intelligence, he could switch over, instead, to the University, and learn something easy, like Latin and Greek.

Every time I returned from a visit to Oxford I felt glad that I had not gone there as a student. Because I was satisfied that I would never have been able to learn anything there. I would have been too much impressed with the buildings, which were not in any way what I had expected them to be, but were all low on to the earth, with rough-looking walls – real mediaeval bricks covered over with a yellowed mediaeval plaster.

I have seen many a stately pile, heavily incrusted with history, thick with dust and tradition, sanctified through the intimacy of its association with a nation's fortunes, through the centuries a silent witness of dooms and splendours – I have seen such a building, cathedral, abbey, palace, mausoleum, and I have not been impressed.

But because the walls of Oxford did not tower, but seemed sunk into the earth, almost, and because with what was venerable about the masonry that had lasted from the Middle Ages there went also a warmth and richness of life that time could not chill, I realised that if I had gone there as a student, I would never have been able to do any work in the place. I would have gone to Oxford and spent too many years in the more idle kind of dreaming.

And talking about people going to University reminds me of Franco's Moors, who on their way to Madrid captured the Spanish capital's University City, and because it was a seat of learning, they sat down there for several years. They tarried in these halls of wisdom, within the friendly cloisters sheltering them from Republican artillery, and they rolled their home-made cigars in pages torn from ancient tomes.

And if none of Franco's mercenaries acquired any doctorates in the course of their two-year sojourn in Madrid University, it is nevertheless certain that their attitude towards life must have undergone some sort of modification in the direction of academicism. And as a result of having crouched down for a prolonged period on the floors of ruined lecture theatres, there is no doubt that when fighting was over, and they eventually emerged from the University City and marched into the streets of Madrid, quite a number of these Moors of Franco's must have walked with a scholarly stoop.

Then there is Wits. I was a student at the Witwatersrand University in the early days, when there was still the smell of wet paint and drying concrete about the buildings at Milner Park, and there was something in my eighteen-year-old soul that revolted at all this newness – and when I went there recently, to attend a play in the Main Hall, I was still appalled at the feeling that Wits had not acquired any of the external characteristics of poise and suavity. The girl who sold me a programme was gauche.

When I was a student at Wits I had a contempt both for the buildings and the professors. I could not reconcile myself to the idea that any really first-class man from Europe would bring himself to apply for so obscure and – as I then thought – Philistine – an appointment as a professorship in a South African mining-town university where the reinforced concrete slabs were still wet inside.

Needless to say, my views in this regard have since that time undergone a very profound change. I have seen some of the things that first-class men get reduced to doing in this life. Myself included. And I feel only a sense of humble gratitude towards those men from overseas who came to the Witwatersrand University when it was first started, bringing with them that vital breath of culture that includes the Near East and Alexandria and the Renaissance, that rich Old World of thought in whose inspiration alone the soul of man can find a place for its abiding.

The Assistant Registrar informs me that something in the neighbourhood of 11 000 students have passed through the portals of the Witwatersrand University since the time that the new buildings were erected on the Milner Park koppies. This figure is only a rough estimate and may possibly be wrong by several thousands. It would be interesting to know what has happened to all of those 11 000 men and women. Not one of them has achieved to anything very extraordinary up to the present moment, apparently. (If I am misinformed in this connection, I should, of course, be glad to make the necessary emendations.) The University authorities could use this fact to great advantage. In the simple statement that "Witwatersrand University students don't get into the headlines" there is all that can be desired in the way of old-world dignity and correctness of tone.

It is strange how the past all looks like the other day. Before they erected the main gate you could wander all over without knowing when you were inside the University grounds. I remember once when I went to look for a Department that was housed away from the main building. I must have got to the wrong place. Because I asked a man in charge there, "Is this the Philosophical Department of the Witwatersrand University?" And he said, "No, this is the filling-up section of the Lion Brewery."

It was only then that I noticed all those bottles stacked around, and I realised that not even a philosophy class could get through that quantity.

It all depends, of course, on what your view is as to what a University should be. If you believe that a University is an institution where you go to acquire technical knowledge, then it does not particularly matter what the buildings and their surroundings are like. On the other hand, if you believe that you go to a University in order to have things done to you that will make you useless for the requirements of practical life, deepening and enriching your spirit in the process – and either view of the functions of a University is legitimate – then the atmosphere of the place in which you are to spend a number of years is highly important.

There must be tall old trees through whose branches the sunshine falls dappled on the walks. There must be winding lanes and unexpected vistas and sequestered nooks. There must be mildew and ruin and dilapidated facades. There must be aged and crooked corridors and aged and crooked professors. All these advantages – or disadvantages – will no doubt accrue to the Witwatersrand University in time. For while there are two schools of thought on the question as to whether or not a University that is a non-technical seat of learning should be lousy – and I can quote highly venerable authority in this connection – it is unanimously conceded that it should be mouldy.

The Witwatersrand University will grow mellowed with the centuries, with the generations of men and women passing through its doors, and I wish that its future may be fortunate, that the enduring things of the mind may remain, the imperishable nobilities of the spirit that will live on, when the gold mines of the Rand have been worked out and been forgotten, when the mills that crushed the ore have fallen into a long stillness.

And those solecisms about the Witwatersrand University that distressed me as a student will belong with the unremembered past, also.

Royal Processions

On the occasion of the marriage of Princess Elizabeth, London had a Royal Procession. I saw a number of Royal Processions during my stay in England, some ten to fifteen years back.

These processions are colourful affairs; they are got up in good style; and in that one moment of scarlet and gold, when your hat is raised, and there is the thunder of hooves on the ground when the royal carriage is passing, and the air is wild with trumpets and cheering, then you find that your pulse throbs very quickly, and strange thrills are stirring in your heart.

And yet, when it is over, and the crowd surges forward into the roadway, you are left with the feeling that Cecil B. de Mille would have done it differently.

Each time I have seen a Royal Procession, I have tried to detect, in its pageantry, the elements of a Roman triumph. But each time the effect has been a failure. The spirit of Imperial Rome – its drama and its flamboyancy – is still in the world, of course, but it is in Hollywood.

The best place from which to view a procession is the pavement. And the best time to take up a position is at midnight. This involves a twelve-hour wait in the gutter. But if you don't come early you will find that the best stretches of gutter have already been taken up, and you have to content yourself with sitting down on an inferior piece of kerbstone, made of the hardest kind of concrete.

This waiting is very pleasant. And I know what Milton meant when he wrote of those that stand and wait. To me there is always something sublime in the thought of people waiting. Whether it is that they are waiting for a train, or for a king to ride past, or for One whose coming shall bring peace to the children of men.

Near me was a man who sat reading a library book by the light of a candle.

I think I have had more fun waiting with the crowd in the gutter, than at most fashionable functions to which, on various occasions, I have been invited. (By mistake, no doubt.) For one thing, at a society wedding, they always engage a number of detectives to breathe down the back of your neck and make you feel jumpy.

In the early hours of the morning – I didn't know the time – there was some cheering. I enquired the cause.

"It's the English dawn," I was informed.

I said it was very agreeable to hear that. But I wondered how they found out.

This is one of the major difficulties which the English winter presents to a man who is used to blue skies. It is always a problem to distinguish between the kind of darkness that they call night-time, and the other kind of darkness that they call daytime. To the uninitiated, all darkness looks about the same.

When he was told that the dawn had come, the man with the library book blew out what was left of his candle, and went on reading in the dark.

It grew later. I got into conversation with the people around me. They told me lots of things about the Royal Family – things I had never heard of before. And I reciprocated by telling them all sorts of things about General Smuts. Things that I am sure General Smuts had never heard of either.

By and by the wedding guests began driving down the Mall on their way to Westminster Abbey. They all looked very distinguished. Maharajahs and Cabinet Ministers and peeresses and foreign ministers and nobilities.

Afterwards a carriage-load of princesses drove slowly past. I stepped off the pavement, in between two policemen, and blew a platonic kiss at the princesses. One of them stuck her hand out of the window, and waved back at me. But it was the wrong princess. And before I could explain the mistake – namely, that I didn't mean her, but the one next to her, with the black hair – the carriage had passed on.

C'est la vie.

Came the big moment. A spectacular climax of bursting colour and tumultuous cheering and gilded carriages and Horse Guards in dazzling uniforms . . . The King and Queen of England . . . I glanced swiftly at the man with the library book. He was still engrossed in his reading. Not once did he lift his eyes from the printed page. I have often wondered what he came to the procession for.

It was a very successful royal wedding. But I also felt there was something lacking, in respect of mediaeval conceptions of largesse, in the sight of vendors of sausage-rolls hawking their wares among the subdued dusk-to-10.30 throngs in Hyde Park and Green Park and St. James' Park. There were no fat oxen turning on spits at Marble Arch, with free chunks of meat for all who came. There were no mighty vats of nut-brown ale set up in Birdcage Walk. Bring your own tankard.

I obtained a good view of General Hertzog. That was because he held his head up very high. Yet there was a strained look on his face. Perhaps he was trying to remember whether it was the Crown Colonies that Britain had promised to hand over to the Union, or whether it was the Crown Jewels.

Perhaps General Hertzog was only homesick.

And I recalled another South African, who drove through London when Victoria was Queen. They still talk about him there. What did he think about, I wonder, when his carriage swung into St. James' Street? About a Bushveld farm, maybe, and the sun lying yellow on white-washed walls, and the big tree by the dam. And yet I hardly think so. I think it is more reasonable to believe that Paul Kruger was pardonably vain about his triumph. And what he really thought was: "If only the boys in the Rustenburg district could see me now."

It is in their passing that all the world's pageants are the same. The Kings have gone, and the clamour has ended, and the sound of marching men is dying in the distance.

London

The other day I got a letter from a South African in London. The address at the top of the note-paper was 47 King's Road, S.W. 3. That set me off trying to remember which way the numbers ran in King's Road, and before I knew where I was I found myself, for the first time in my life, the victim of a powerful nostalgic influence evoked by the sound of the word "London".

I suppose that as you grow older life starts playing tricks like that with your emotions. Certainly, I should not have imagined that I would ever develop feelings of this description – a sense of romantic pain at the farawayness of a place that during the years in which I stayed there meant little to me beyond the fact that it had millions more people in it than any other city in the world. This was a fact about London that I didn't have to go to look up in a reference book. I observed it all just in one casual glance out of the train window, with the train slowing down at King's Cross.

I insist, however, that what I got was not a feeing of homesickness, when I read that letter from an address in Chelsea. I had not the slightest desire to go back there in reality. But I derived a good deal of harmless pleasure, tinged with that pale melancholy with which all things of the past are invested, in allowing my memory to stray.

Memory is the past held together with pieces of rusty wire. Therewith is the imagination fed and sustained. I believe that if you live under a regime in which you are not permitted to say: "Here's to the old days; the good old days," even if you are saying it only in a spirit of perversity, and even if the old days were very bad old days – then there can't be any poetry produced under that regime.

And when I sigh, "High-ho," like that, for the good old days, it is not out of weariness with the present; it is only to indicate the underneath strains of a poetry getting ready to drop a many-hued translucent veil over endless, frighteningly-cheer-less streets and endless, frighteningly-cheerless rows of chim-ney-pots.

But, of course, London isn't really like that. Unfortunately, however, it took me two years to discover the important fact that the chimney-pots of, say, Fulham, have got nothing to do with the chimney-pots of Walham Green, London actually not being a city at all but consisting of a vast number of villages, each distinct and separate and individual and as different as Trompsburg is from Mossel Bay. Somebody should have told me that on the ship, going over. But nobody did. There were a lot of things of that sort that I had to learn for myself, and that took a long time, whereas I could have got all that kind of information out of textbooks. The trouble was that I had a contempt for textbooks in those days, and I thought I knew better. You know, youth and all that. Youth nurtured on poets' lies. And I don't care: I still think that that's the highest wis-dom, and streets better than common sense. Streets, with end-less rows of chimney-pots, better.

As is well known, I don't believe that there is anything that Europe can teach us. Rather do I believe that Africa has a vast amount of knowledge to impart to a cocksure because decay-ing Europe. There are, nevertheless, times when I feel that we have a couple of things to learn from the northern countries, including England. And one of these things is winter. It is not that our winters aren't cold enough. A winter spell on the Free State highveld can produce an intensity of cold equal, I should say, to anything outside of the arctic circle. But where they have us beat is in regard to the stagery of winter. They put on a full-length show, directed with rare skill and helped out with an impressive assortment of theatre props that are nontheless effective for being old-fashioned and charged with melo-drama: including black skies to contrast with white snow, and fogs and frozen streams. Whereas, in the Free State, on a cold day, you just stand and shiver. It is cold enough, but lacking in the theatrical. You haven't got the proper stage equipment. This is a deficiency that has to be put right before we can have the atmosphere, in this country, for proper haunted-house stories. The haunted houses themselves we've got.

What we are short of are the haunted winters.

Anyway, that letter from an address in Chelsea awakened a flow of memories that are, surprisingly enough, happy. Maybe it is only part of the enchantment that time lends. Nevertheless, I shouldn't like to go back there – not for keeps, anyway. I'm not pining for the place. It is just that, latterly, in the midst of my everyday activities here in Johannesburg, I have been catching glimpses of other, older scenes. A piece of white wall overgrown by an oak in Saratoga Avenue, Doornfontein, in the rain, has suddenly brought back Maida Vale. A current of steamy air, laden with the smell of cooking, has raised up before me, on a Commissioner Street corner, a Lyons tearoom in Pimlico.

And only yesterday, while I was talking to a man in a flat in Hillbrow, I got a feeling as if – but it's all right; they can't lure me back to London with soft stuff. It is only natural that when you have spent a considerable part of your life in any place, you should afterwards become imbued with a sense of having left some portion of yourself behind, there. Indeed, only a few weeks ago, while I was on holiday at the coast, I lived for a few days in a hired tent. And because for a brief period that tent pitched on a vacant stand had been home to me, I noticed on the morning when I raised the flap and issued from the tent for the last time, that I walked out with a sigh.

Consequently, when I suddenly found myself thinking that it would be rather nice, at this moment, to be strolling down Brompton Road again, then I realise that it is an unprofitable sort of wish – just like wanting to go to have another look at that hired tent pitched on a stretch of sloping ground in the Tsitsikama.

And I would never be so foolish as to go and do anything unprofitable. Oh, no, of course not. It is not my nature to. But there was something about that tent, the way it sagged between two tentpoles – oh, well, perhaps I will manage to get around to viewing it again, some time.

Class Snobbery in Britain

The effect of England's political swing-over to the Left will no doubt be far-reaching. For England, I mean. Because this last general election, like each one that preceded it, has been the most vital in history.

It should be interesting to re-visit England in about five years' time, in order to ascertain at first hand the changes that have been brought about, by the war and the Labour Government, in the social structure of England and in the outlook and mode of life of that large class – I forget what its proportion is of the total population – that constitutes the upper stratum.

Centuries ago there were three classes in England – upper, middle and lower. In the course of time, and most particularly during the Victorian era, the middle class began to merge with the upper. (I am only going by what they told me over there: but it seems to make sense.) The result is that there has of recent years been only one line of class cleavage in England that is clearly demarcated, and that is the yawning gulf or the gaping abyss or the dizzy-making abyss that separates the upper classes from the rest of the population.

I found, in the England of from 12 years ago until the early part of the war, that this thing of class difference was as concrete as a siege-gun emplacement. And because it continued without a break during those years in which I lived in England, I assumed that this state of affairs must have been going on for quite a while before that, also. For a millennium or two, maybe. And it is not inconceivable that it is an order of things which might survive even the war and the Labour Government.

The basis of this distinction – what it consists in – is something that I have never been able to determine satisfactorily. It isn't wholly a matter of money: at least, I don't think so. Take that vast hotel population that is located in Bayswater, W. 2. You might, I suppose, term the residents of this hotel area, that is in itself the size of a city, the dregs of the upper and middle class. But that wouldn't be correct. (Not that those people would care what you called them, of course.) The fact is that from the point of view of speech, status-outlook, culture and refinement – both in the possession and the lack of these attributes – these people clearly and unmistakably belong to the upper order. And many of them are very poor. I wonder whether the percentage with a private income of over six hundred a year is at all considerable. So it isn't a question of money, really.

No, the basic nature of this distinction in class between one person you come across in the street and another is by no means clear to the outside observer. At the same time, it is a difference that goes deeper than flesh and bone and deeper than any plummet. It is a difference not of genus, but of species. And when you are in doubt about a person's class the best thing is to ask some member of the lower orders about him. The upper class can make mistakes in these matters. The lower classes, never. A member of the working class knows infallibly in the same way that a costermonger never goes wrong. It doesn't matter what clothes you wear. Buy a couple of bananas from a costermonger and he will know, right on the turn, in handing you your change, whether to address you as sir or mate.

But maybe the effects of war and the Labour Government will alter all this. Maybe, in future, when a broken-down noble-man is reduced to doing a spot of road repairs for a living – with cement on his waistcoat and his trouser-legs tied up with string, just below the knees; when this broken-down noble-man accidentally strikes a passing Cockney with his pick, maybe the Cockney, rubbing the sore place, isn't going to remark, "Cheese that, guvnor." Maybe England is going to change as much as all that. But perhaps what I have cited is too obvious an example. After all, it is only a gentleman that can be as careless as all that with a pick. Like, in shootin', not drawing too fine a distinction between a partridge and a beater.

We are now brought, after one or two minor digressions, to a consideration of what I believe to be the underlying principle that determines the application of th English caste system. It is a mental hygiene test. It has got to do with sanity.

Can you reason clearly? Are you rational? Does your mind function in terms of accepted and well-understood logical sequences? Yes? Then you fall into the lower sort of category. Whereas, your claims to gentility are decided in terms of the degree to which you are classifiable as barmy. I applied this rule on a fairly extensive scale in England. I don't think I had any misses.

Some time ago I read a story about an Irish girl who married into an English aristocracy. A year or so after her marriage some friends of hers in Ireland were discussing her.

"What's it like for her?" somebody asked, "Is she happy there? Does she feel at home at all, living with the English nobility?"

"It was difficult for her at first," was the reply. "She couldn't understand her husband's people, or they her. But it's different now. She has been like one of them ever since she fell off her horse, on her head, and got concussion."

That's it in a nutshell. The test based on psychopathology.

Thus, in England, if you are talking to somebody, and his conversation makes sense, and it is illuminated by the light of reason, you can be sure that he is a member of the lower orders. And if his thoughts are expressed with marked clarity, suggestive of his having an unusually good, sound brain, you can almost work out on what street corner his news-stand is situated.

I was once resident for a while in a hotel near Princes' Square. The guests were of the better class, and included a retired Church of England clergyman, a number of gentlemen whose occupation varied from that of making detailed observations of swan and duck life at the muddier end of the Serpentine to the construction of paper darts, barbed with broken pen-nibs, for throwing at the ceiling, and a large number of women who were all, in various ways, amusingly indifferent to what went on in the world of external reality.

113

One day the proprietress of the hotel took me outside. "A gentleman from South Africa will be coming to stay here from tomorrow," she told me, "and I am afraid that he might want to leave after the first day. You know what it is. Like in the lounge, for instance, with Mrs. Holdgate always slapping poor Miss Younger – and other things. I shall be glad if you will explain to this gentleman from South Africa that the rather better class of English society – well, it's like this. He won't find things any different in any other hotel – unless it is one of those common commercial places in the West End. So if you will say just a few words to him –"

I promised.

The gentleman from South Africa arrived. He was a member of a very old and well-established Cape family. In his luggage was an instrument composed of a number of reeds. He confided to me that he had been practising, for upwards of seventeen years, in an amateur way, on this instrument which he had himself invented, with a view to reproducing accurately the sounds made by some of our better-known domestic animals. He thought he had almost perfected one sound. I saw right away that there was no need for me to explain to my fellow-South African about the other guests. He went into the lounge, in the evening, and saw nothing wrong with anything that went on there. He played his reed instrument to himself and none of the guests saw anything wrong with him, either. He was accepted. Deep had called unto deep. This scion of an old Cape family was as good class as they were.

And that's about all there seems to be to this English class-distinction business. Commenting on the privileged classes, some people say that what they suffer from is decadence. Other people – and I share this view – say there is nothing wrong with them at all. They have got some very good qualities, which I don't need to go into here, and they are not nearly as snobbish or exclusive as the working class, the members of which I found to be smugly and, if I may say so, quite distressingly class-conscious.

"I am only a working man, but –" seems to me to be the most

unfortunately self-righteous platitude that there is in the whole world.

Maybe the war and the Labour Government will alter that, too.

Rebuilding Europe's Cities

Now that peace has come to Europe – or has it? – it is not uninteresting to speculate on the face that cities of Western Europe will be wearing now. There will be changes, of course, in some of them, obviously enough, of a quite startling nature. For one thing, there will be rebuilding to be done and on a scale for which we can find, off-hand, only the word unprecedented. This applies to a by no means insignificant area of Europe. Cities that have been laid in ruin and for whose reconstruction totally new plans have got to be drawn up.

It is to be trusted that the commissionaires of public works in the various countries will apply a certain measure of imagination to the exercising of their official functions – a difficult task for works commissionaires, whose imaginative powers appear to have declined considerably since that Egyptian dynasty which saw the building of Thebes. At all events, we hope that the works commissionaires, in resurrecting ruins, will be requested to distinguish between ancient and modern. That they don't go and erect pillar-boxes where a Gothic castle used to stand. Or replacing the fallen pillars of the Parthenon with steel and concrete structures. Or set about macadamising the Appian Way.

Anyway, it must be a tough job, after a city has been destroyed, to have to build it up all over again, from scratch, as it were. And I bet the new lot of architects and town planners and building contractors will make just about the same mistakes as the old ones did. They will create the same ugliness and the same choas. It may be difficult to achieve all that – but they will. That much is comforting.

Civic authorities will once more have to wrack their brains in the planning of the thoroughfares, so as to ensure the creation of bottlenecks and the maximum amount of congestion. They will have to put railway stations in all the wrong places they can think of. Law courts will once more have to be constructed to look like museums, and town halls to look like town halls and art galleries to look like gas-works. And as a result, the cities of bombed Europe will again become impossible bedlams and therefore places that you can live in. In a city centrally planned in terms of Utopian conceptions the soul of man perishes.

In Ostend I once lived for a short period in premises immediately above a very ancient and dilapidated cinema. No seat cost more than 5 francs: for soldiers 1 fr. 75 cent, partout. The solitary usherette was very old and very drunk. Her shoulders were draped in a time-yellowed scarf that was always falling off. She had a nervous habit of suddenly shooting her hand up to her throat to feel if the scarf was still there. I realised how much this aged usherette had become part of the cinema. In my imagination I saw that scarf as one with the plaster sliding off the walls of the picture theatre.

From the orthodox commissioner-of-works' point of view, a cinema like that in a town would be a standing civic disgrace.

But see how convenient it was for me. I merely had to get out of bed, slip my trousers on over my pyjamas, step into my shoes, hang on my overcoat over the lot – it was winter – and within two minutes of having been asleep I would be watching a film. A quick change of this description was not only a metamorphosis. It was life. The change of one dream world for another.

One day a neighbour in those premises on top of the cinema spoke to me about my daily visits to the pictures.

"Yes," I said, "They are very old pictures, but there is a change of programme three times a week."

"But it is not necessary," my neighbour explained, shaking his head.

"I know it is not necessary," I replied, "but when I am on holiday I don't mind seeing the same film over twice."

For answer my neighbour conducted me into his small flat on the other side of the passage. He closed the door and switched off the light. Apparently the floor of the apartments overhead served as the ceiling of the cinema. At all events, through that hole in the floor I could obtain a reasonably clear view of what was taking place on the silver screen.

"It is not necessary to go down there," my neighbour assured me, "where it is so draughty."

I understood, now, where the draughts came from . . .

I declined the invitation, however. It was, of course, a lot more comfortable to watch the programme from inside that man's flat than to go and sit downstairs in the draught where the drunken usherette was, and the public and the crumbling plaster. But it wasn't the same thing. So I thanked my neighbour and withdrew, having the presence of mind, however, first to drop my cigarette-end through the hole in the floor.

I don't believe that this cinema was ever bombed. I feel sure that the old thing just collapsed on its own, suddenly, one day in the middle of a film show, and that the audience simply filed out with the feeling that the management was getting more thoughtless in regard to the comfort of its patrons every day.

That cinema building had atmosphere. It had life.

All this talk of rebuilding the bombed cities of Europe in terms of long-range utilitarian conceptions and architectural vision would, of course, be very terrible, if it didn't remain all talk. But we know jolly well that it is all talk, and so we don't even resign ourselves to it.

A plan is only all right if it is drawn up to accord with human nature. It may have all sorts of excellencies and perfections, otherwise, but if it doesn't fit in with human nature it just won't work. And human nature is sloppy and sentimental and brutal and defiant and despicable and reaching out for the sublimities and drunken. That is why, if you say a man is a god, you won't go far wrong; and if you want to call him a thing lower than the beasts, you won't go far wrong, either.

The cities of Europe will rise again out of their rubble. Their streets will wind along the banks of the rivers on which they are situated. They will conform with sea-fronts and hills and valleys and the demands of propertied and privileged interests. And from a peaceful movement one will again become confronted with a spectacle as violently outre as the Arches of Adelphi. In spite of the planners, life will creep back into the cities. And into the buildings drama of a kind that the architects did not intend.

I believe that the war will have made no difference to the cities of Europe. A city gets its individuality from the people who lived there. The streets get torn up; the buildings get destroyed; the soul of the place remains.

I looked out of a window in Paris one night. The streets were silent. Pieces of torn paper fluttered in the chill wind. And I sensed – with a strange sort of emotion – that there was something different about these fragments of torn paper merely because the night wind was blowing them through a Paris street.

The city in which a genius has lived becomes recreated into something that is more than the inanimate background to his source. The streets through which he has walked much. The scenes amid which the incomprehensible pattern of his life unfolded. Above all, the places where sublime inspiration came to him. It doesn't matter what happens to such a place, afterwards. That spot on the earth's surface remains impregnated with a spirit of beauty that is forever rich and rare. Take a stroll through the streets of Brussels and you will see what I mean.

The artistic soul of a city is the contribution that genius makes to it. Its incongruities are the things that life brings along: the architects and the city planners and the landowners and human nature. And you can't do without either influence.

When a city has got enough incongruities I feel that you can live in it.

For life to be possible in a city there has to be reproduced, on a large scale, the atmosphere of what I tried to convey as having existed in miniature, in that old picture-theatre of Ostend.

Above all, a city must have strong and bizarre contrasts. Ermines and rags. Beauty and filth. The sublime and the diabolical. A well-conducted night club operating next door to a perhaps not so well-conducted morgue.

I have thought of a story that I would like to write some day, when I get time.

It is about people who live in Johannesburg and people who live, say, in the Marico Bushveld. These two sets of people, those who live in city flats and those who live on the farm, don't know each other. They never meet. But life does exactly the same things to each of them. Life is like that. And the story ends with the heroine of this little group of people in the city, smashed into pieces by the things life has done to her, declaring that she can't stand it any longer: she has got to get away, somewhere. And the girl on the farm, to whom exactly the same things have happened, says this has been too terrible. She is going to Johannesburg. What she means is life. Life . . .

The difference between the city and the farm is, alas, age-old. The city has gutters.

Writing

The older I grow, the more puzzled I get as to what life is for and how to live it.

Since my early adolescence I have had one fervent longing: to have twelve months of leisure in which I should be able to devote myself in exclusiveness and abandonment to the task of writing the things that have surged blindly inside me for expression. Just a quiet room somewhere and a piece of floor-space to lie down on, and pen and ink, and a ream of 34-lb. cream-laid paper cut into quarto size. That is the one thing I have wanted all my life, and always it has evaded me. There have been times when I have seemed on the verge of achieving to this ambition, and then on each occasion what has seemed to be the beginning of this period of leisure has in actual fact been but the prelude to fresh turmoil, the calm before the storm.

I can always get the ream of cream-laid easily enough, and my connections with the printing industry make it a simple matter for me to get a quad-cap ream cut up into the right sized sheets, and ink is cheap. A piece of quiet floor-space and a strip of hessian to lie on, though more difficult to procure, are not completely beyond the range of my organisational capacity. But it is then, when I have got all these things together, and I am well set on Act 1, Scene 1 of a sublime, high tragedy, and I have got to "Enter Bernadus van Aswegen" – it is then that the outside world enters with shouting and banners, and I proceed to roll up my strip of hessian and I sighfully set a light to the 48 lb. cream-laid, and I take the nib out of the pen-holder and break off the points and fasten a strip of folded paper to the back of it, and shoot it into the ceiling.

I don't remember, just offhand, how many times in my life I have got as far as "Enter Bernadus van Aswegen" – and at that point the world has entered, swearing and flat-footedly trampling. Sometimes it has been creditors. On one occasion it was the bailiffs. Once it was a demolition gang come to tear down the building. Once, also it was the police. And always I have had to get up from the floor, with Bernardus' momentous opening speech unwritten.

I have got so, now, that I accept it as inevitable that there is a curse on Bernadus van Aswegen; he is bad luck; he will never be allowed to walk on to the centre of the stage, his brow furrowed in thought, his right arm raised dramatically to say: ". . ." But it is O.K. I won't write down the opening words of his speech, which I know off by heart just as well as he does. I don't want this article to be interrupted, also. I have learnt cunning with the years.

And with the years I have begun, in some strange fashion, to identify myself with Bernadus van Aswegen. I feel that the world won't allow him to have his say, any more than it will allow me to have my say. It gives me a queer sense of intimacy with Bernadus. What he feels, I feel. His hopes are my hopes. And we have both learnt this same truth from life. Bernadus and I – and it is knowledge as ineluctable as death – and that is that we are both doomed to eternal frustration every time we really want to open our mouths.

And I regret to say that with the years Bernadus van Aswegen has begun to grow embittered. There is today a cynical twist to the left part of his upper lip that I don't like. It doesn't help him to win and keep friends. And it is no use my trying to reason with him, either. "Aren't I as good as Lear?" he asks of me. "What has Othello got that I haven't got? And you know I can make rings round Hamlet, can't I?" "Well, Bernadus," I reply, "I wouldn't say rings. But as good, yes. And there is that soliloquy I've got for you on the death of your little daughter. But I started it all so long ago, and we have both grown so old in the meantime that I am afraid it will now have to be your little granddaughter. And there is that opening speech, right in the beginning, in the first scene, when you say . . ."

"Oh, cut it out," Bernadus replies petulantly, "I never get so far. If it isn't creditors it's men with picks and shovels. Or it's a couple of 'johns' from Marshall Square."

"Don't use such dreadful solecisms, Bernadus," I answer, soothingly. "Remember you are a character in a great tragedy. Don't say 'johns'."

And so it goes on.

But I am trying to write of life and its meaning, if any, and I have reluctantly come to accept a conclusion that has been persistently forced on me by external circumstance. And I can't evade this conclusion. Within my experience the same situation has repeated itself over and over again. I believe that, speaking strictly for myself personally, the practising of the creative art of letters is contrary to the laws and demands of life. It is always when I have turned out my best work, and I have got the right sort of recognition for it, too, in terms of people dubiously enquiring as to whether I think that I should go on writing at all – it is at these times, when my creative powers, such as they are, have been at their peak, that the worst kinds of disasters have invariably overtaken me.

And this is something I can't understand. I have become afraid to pick up the pen. Or, when I do, to dip it in too deep.

And this is something that, I have noticed, applies to other writers as well. Recently I read another biography on Edgar Allan Poe, in which the story of his life is related with a strict regard to chronology. I got to 1845. This year, states the biographer, was a year of great literary creativeness for Edgar Allan Poe. "Next year, 1846," I thought, "Edgar Allan Poe will have dropped in the . . ." I read on and found that, by 1846, he had.

Taking it by and large, it is far better not to write.

But I think I have solved the problem of Bernadus van Aswegen. I shall keep him out of the play until right at the end. He will enter only in the last scene of Act V. He comes on at the opposite-prompt side. He knows his lines. He walks on to the centre of the stage and raises his right hand, and just as he opens his mouth the curtain falls. Title: *Bernadus van Aswegen, A Tragedy in Five Acts.*

Building and Buildings

The report in the Press about an architect's resignation because his plans for the rebuilding of Coventry Cathedral had been rejected, was of more than passing interest to me. For I am fascinated by all the departments of that very ancient art of giving expression to imaginative conceptions through the medium of earth and stone.

The ruins of a temple reared to a forgotten god; a pile of crumbling masonry; an unroofed edifice whose sightless walls are a reminder of a nobler day; a column prone in the long grass. This sort of thing always gets me. I like an old building, no matter how decrepit it is. I don't care much for an old building when it has been restored.

But I have never been able to take naturally to a cathedral. For one thing, there is so much you have to learn about it. Things like nave and aisle and transept and apse: lots of terms that apply only to a cathedral, and exclusively to a cathedral, and that you can't apply to the architecture of a town hall or a prison or a grocery store. And I am not very fond of words like that.

And then there is the arched roof of the cathedral, leaping dizzily away from the earth, so that it isn't safe to look up unless you first clutch on to a piece of stray statuary, or lay hold of the railings around the tomb of a crusader.

Whenever I have been in a cathedral, and I have seen a woman gazing aloft, it has always come as a surprise to me that her skirts did not fly up over her head. That is the feeling I get inside a cathedral, when it is a good cathedral, and the architect and the builders have made a satifactory job of it. I get a sensation of a vast upward rush through infinite space and a tumult of high winds. All that sense of abstract tracklessness terrifies me. I don't like it. I feel in the presence of all that aerial space that I want something human and cosy. I want the stink of warm life and of cold death, even, to make me feel at home again on the earth.

I can't stand that violent movement into emptiness which I experience when I gaze skyward under the arched roof of a cathedral. Put me down in the old crypt, however, and I am quite all right.

Another reason, too, I think, why I can't take readily to a cathedral, no matter how ancient it is, is because I can't sense in it the romance of human habitation. Throughout the centuries the people who entered the cathedral came there as visitors, and they wore their Sunday clothes, and they were on their best behaviour, and they were quite unnatural. They came there in a spirit of religious awe, and they felt good, somehow, and solemn, somehow, under the vault through which they could see the sky; and they thought that God was there – forgetting that He was in their homes, where they lived, and in the taverns, and in the market place where money changed hands.

At least half of the fascination that an old building has for me lies in its human associations.

And I like an old building to be squat and heavy. It must have thick walls and a lot of bulk, and the less window apertures it has, the better I like it. A lowering hulk of brick or stone, sombre and blackened with time and sullen and brooding: that is the kind of old building that you can't tear me away from: I just don't want to know.

And I don't want a guide, either, to lead me about the gloomy corridors of an old place like that, or to acquaint me with its history. Because I can see its history in those stones. I can sense more about that old building that any guidebook could tell me. I can feel who the people were that came there, and why, and what were the things that went on in their minds. Things that the compiler of a guidebook would be astonished to learn, no doubt.

The building of cities is an activity that has been going on for thousands of years, and in its essentials it has not altered from the dawn of civilisation. The building operations connected with the rearing of the towers of Ilium must have been pretty similar to the processes involved in the construction of a Roman aqueduct or a Carthaginian temple, or a Norman castle or a present-day super cinema.

First the architect would get to work on a piece of paper with his pencil and ruler and compasses and he would say to the baron, in the historical novelist's language of the period (assuming that it is the Middle Ages and that it is a castle that is going to be built) "Now, would your lordship fain have your embrasures with ye plain bevelled openings, or doth my lord's mind incline to the sort which is at the nonce in great demand in France, and which hath ye holes for pouring through ye molten lead?"

"Oh, the molten lead ones," the baron would answer with alacrity, holding the plans upside down.

"And will it please my lord to have his arches underpinned and his squinches groined?"

"Yea, I got to have that," the baron would reply, not knowing what it was all about, but determined not to reveal his ignorance.

"And would my lord as lief instal ye launcet-windows for your keep?" the architect would continue.

"How do you mean, my keep?" the baron would demand, growing slightly irritable at having to answer so many intimate questions, "I keep myself. And the rest I make out of occasional forays and sorties."

"Nay, nay, my lord, ye keep signifieth ye donjon, ye inner part of the ye castel – where your lordship doth abide. Will my lordship have ye launcet-windows for ye keep?"

"Anything as long as it keeps out the fresh air," the feudal lord would say. "But why can't you talk proper English?"

Anyway, I don't know the meaning either – any more than the mediaeval baron did – of the terms employed in the science of building. But their poetry haunts me. And I want to know more about them. Like there are lots more things in the world that I want to know more about, not only out of books, but from practical experience. And to me it is one of the mysteries of life that we mortals are afforded so little leisure for pursuing the paths we would really like to tread.

I personally would like to spend many years in ennobling my mind with the study of ancient and useless lore. It is true that I have already acquired, more by accident than design, a fair working knowledge of quite a number of subjects serving no good purpose. But I want my mind still further ennobled by the study of much more useless ancient things. A man told me the other day that scientific development has reached the stage where it will shortly be possible for mankind to leave the earth and set about colonising the planets and other bodies of outer space. That would suit me fine. We who have no spiritual contact with science and progress could then be left alone to do what we like. We shall grow grapes and make wine and read old books.

But to return to building construction as it was carried on through past ages. I am interested in the different systems of measurement they used, and in the things they said. Ells and cubits and feet and roods. "Give him a span and he'll take a Gothic league." And, "who's been smoothing this wall with my new cubit rule?"

I wonder, too, what sort of tools the masons used. Even to-day a bricklayer doesn't need much more than a trowel and a square and a plumb-line. But then, he hasn't got to build a pyramid, of course. ("I am one of the oldest hands on this Sphinx: I started when they was still on the legs . . . And it's all a riddle to me.")

And I am also interested to know how the builders mixed their mortar in the world's vanished civilisations. What kind of cement did they add to the sifted sand before they poured on water? There are so many things I should like to know about the way the world's work was done in the past. Not that I want to do it all myself, of course. I am only intensely interested in how the ancients set about these things.

Somewhere at the back of my mind I have got a feeling that I can't quite put into words. I feel that why a building fascinates me is because, when it is completed, with the last piece of inside woodwork sand-papered and the last nail-hole filled in with putty, and the masons and carpenters and painters have left, then there has come into the world a new piece of creation. Somebody conceived a vision, and the workmen gave that man's dream outward shape. In his mind a man conceived that building whole and the builders set about interpreting his conception in terms of the earth's most primitive materials of soil and stone. So that in the construction of this building what has taken place is really a magical thing. It is as though the man that got the vision cast a spell which brought about the external realisation of his dream. And from this point of view every building is enchanted, and every city is fairy.

The Norman baron's castle is a castle in Spain.

Calling All Patients

The other day I took ill – a slight twinge in my right leg, a twinge going up and down, sort of. I sent for a doctor. This reminded me of that "short prose narrative" of O. Henry's, which begins "So I Went to See a Doctor". Now, that story is one of my O. Henry favourites, and I have often wondered what did happen in that New York medical practitioner's consulting-room about half a century ago. I have also thought that the story would be very interesting told the other way around – i.e., bearing the title "So I Went to See O. Henry," and related by the doctor.

But that was not to be. For O. Henry could still walk, and so he walked into where the doctor was, and got examined, and after that walked out again. And so I expect that the only official record of the visit to the doctor by the then still unknown man of genius consisted of a number of unimaginative entries in the doctor's notebook. In the column headed, "Name of Patient," there would probably be nothing more than "Mr. W. S. Porter," and under "Diagnosis," just that familiar annotation that has such time-honoured links with the science of healing: "Drunk."

Here is something to reflect on, now. You never hear of a case in which the patient enters the doctor's consulting room and after a brief interview with the doctor – who has stood in the middle of the floor, swaying – the patient walks out and, before stepping into the lift, makes this entry in his own notebook: "Diagnosis of Doctor's condition – Drunk."

Oh, no, that sort of thing never happens. It is always the poor patient that gets unflattering remarks about himself written down in a well-bound appointment book for thoughtless people to get mirthful over in after years. Remarks like "Gen. N. Bonaparte" – "Fallen Arches," or "Sir Walter Raleigh" – "Ye Mange," or "P. B. Shelley" – "Bog Spavined," or "Miss. C. Bronte" – "Blue-Tongue." Small wonder, therefore, that the patient has begun to break down under the weight of opprobrium and ridicule with which during the centuries his lot has been burdened – in fact, ever since Hippocrates first wrote (in B.C. 420) behind a sick man's name, in good Greek, "Alcibiades, Esq., – Goofball Addict."

But it is quite different with doctors, of course. I mean, for one thing, it has been proved that doctors are never addicted to drugs. The reason is quite obvious. Because he has constant access to every kind of dope there is, a doctor is not tempted to become a drug fiend. A couple of lungfuls of opium out of the old bamboo pipe just before breakfast does the average doctor until lunch-time. The early forenoon cocaine habit it not nearly as widespread among the members of the medical fraternity as the lay public imagines. Similarly, a whiff or two of Indian hemp, supplemented by a shot of morphia or codeine, sees the medical man through the particularly trying period which mid-afternoon is to most workers. And when he goes off duty he is quite content with a heroin injection, or with a few grains of fly agaric or Banisteria caapi. All of which goes to prove that while the patient is every kind of moron and disease-carrier and sot, the doctor is none of these things.

So that when a doctor looks at you with a fixed, glassy stare, you *know* (because it has been proved) that he is not drugged. He has got that dazed expression of a man listening to enchanting harmonies – and as if the bonds of time and space are broken – just through over-work. And when he acts queer, as though suffering from sensorial illusions – well, he's just thinking, that's all. Sensorial illusions, my foot. It's not the patient we're dealing with now.

Anyway, as a result of my having got that aforementioned twinge, I was suddenly able to see life from what was to me a novel angle. I realised that with all this medical progress business, and all this eulogising of people like Pasteur and Lister and Jennings, there was one person in grave danger of being overlooked – namely, the patient. Where would medical science be without the patient – lying in bed on his back, with one leg raised in the air, or just lying on his back? Or being wheeled on a trolley with the blankets pulled over his head after an operation? Or having the screens drawn around his bed at a solemn nod from the doctor, also after an operation? . . . The person at the very core of every situation concerned with the treatment of disease or injury is none other than the patient.

Calling Dr. Kildare. That's quite all right. But of what earthly use is Dr. Kildare, unless there's Patient Willemse first? You could go on calling Dr. Kildare until you were blue in the face, else. What the world has hitherto overlooked is the fact that the backbone of medical science and the Hollywood film industry is the hospital patient.

This is an injustice that I hope to see righted still within my own lifetime – a period not likely to be unduly extended in view of the fact that I am receiving daily treatment at the General Hospital, although it be only as an out-patient.

What is needed is a series of medical films on the lines of *Pasteur, The Story of Dr. Erlich, Calling Dr. Kildare, Dr. Jekyll and Mr. Hyde, Men in White* and the rest of them, but with this difference, that the accent is shifted slightly, so that the hero-surgeon is replaced by the hero-patient. A few titles of this newer sort of film that I can think of just off-hand are *Hospital Patient O'Higgins, Calling Patient O'Higgins, Patient O'Higgins's Last Op, Curtains for Patient O'H.*

For *Men in White* we could substitute *Men in Bed*, or *Men in Pyjamas* or – for a period film – *Men in Long Nightshirts* (in Technicolor perhaps). Another film in this series would be *Men in Dressing-Gowns*, meaning the convalescents sitting on the stoep in wheelchairs – survivors of spectacular major operations . . . But, naturally, there are not so many in this class – c.f., *Patient O'Higgins's Last Op.* (And also *Curtains for Patient O'H.*) So *Men in Dressing-Gowns* could possibly just be made into an educational short.

Some day, when I have time to do a spot of research work, I would like to compile a volume on *Great Hospital Patients of the World.* Typical passages, dealing with typical pioneer patients, would read something after this style:

"There was no incentive for Heinrich B. Zoss (1857-1887) to leave his own country, Germany, to become a patient in new

131

hospitals across the seas. The patients of those days had no hope of becoming famous men . . . His arguments were denounced by all the eminent patients of his native land . . . In despair he fled to Vienna, where he achieved his life's ambition of being acupunctured and moxibustioned within the same week, which was, strangely enough, also destined to be his last week . . ."

Or again: "Switzerland's pioneer hospital patient showed no unusual gifts as a boy for that brilliant career which, but for the jealousy of certain famous contemporaries, would have terminated in his being elected a Fellow of the Board of International Patients . . . Born in a charcoal-burner's hut, like many another patient of humble origin, he rose to be one of the leading patients at the Zurich Hospital, where, in the course of a brief but memorable career, he (just) lived to see his intestines divided into etc., etc. . . ."

Or this one: "Before closing the chapter on American patients, the name of Oswald Sauerbach must not be forgotten . . . Known as 'the stormy petrel of American hospital wards,' Sauerbach early in life advanced the startling theory that etc., etc. . . . The doctor who eventually performed this operation on Oswald Sauerbach lived to become a world-famous Professor of Surgery. Oswald did not."

Calling Patient Willemse. Calling Patient Willemse. Calling Patient Willemse. No reply. Patient Willemse has had his chips. (Cf., *Patient O'Higgins's Last Op*).

History

The word history conjures up tremendous things to the imagination. Pageantry and princes, bishops, richly apparelled courtiers, thrones, treasures, jewellery, banners and flamboyance – and, occasionally, a dull thud.

The earth is a history book. Sermons in stones, Legends in coal-seams. Facts in clay. Epics, of course, in dust.

But since the awakening of the world to the coming of the gods Nature has been less accurate in the records she keeps. Her chronicles have been one-sided. Of late, she has introduced too much propaganda into her history books. Too much about the will to power; not enough about the full moon.

But the advantage that Nature's story has is that it is easy to read. It can be followed with much less strain than a school history book: the same way that it is so much easier to read poetry than the daily newspaper. But then, of course, the fault with poetry is that it is not literary. Similarly, Nature deals not in literature but in ideas. Not in a setting but in a fancy.

The important difference between history as man writes it and as Nature writes it is that man's records are all rather solemn and awe-inspiring, whereas Nature indulges almost exclusively in low comedy.

In Nature's history book there is much excellent fooling. In this respect I think it would be a distinct contribution to the cause of higher education to compile a list, with succinct annotations, of *Comic Characters in World History*. This list would include, say, the pious Aeneas, Thoth, Sir Galahad, Martin Luther, Erasmus, Thomas A. Beckett, Solon, the late Goethe, Confucius, Nebuchadnezzar, Frederick the Great, Woodrow Wilson, Elizabeth Fry, St. Bartholomew, and the Last of the Mohicans. (Ain't we got fun?)

It would, of course, be possible to extend this list considerably without entering upon controversial ground, and without becoming vulgar.

I would have liked also to have lengthened this list to have included *Comic Characters in South African History*. The field here is remarkably good. It would be a sonorous and instructive register, including say – but no, I must refrain. My educational purpose is almost certain to be misunderstood.

From the crudely comic we pass inevitably to the more purposeful side of history. It expresses itself most characteristically in acts associated with the release of the latent energy in high explosive compounds.

The invention of gunpowder marks an important departure in the history of man. It is strange to reflect that the Roman Empire finally fell in cannon-smoke. It is strange to recall that the purple and gold of an empire which in its dim origins had had direct contact with the Argonauts, survived ponderously the attack of the archer and the spear-carrier, to mingle with the sand only as modern empires fall, to the thunder of the guns.

When dealing with history it is unfortunately impossible to avoid some reference to this aspect of it that can most conveniently be condensed as Dirty Work in the Corridors of Time.

There is a lot of this sort of thing in world history. Indeed, there is actually a war in progress at the time of writing. In its way, of course, the present war may be regarded as not unimportant. In the magnitude of the cultural and social issues involved it cannot, of course, be compared with the wars between Athens and Sparta. Nor in its probably ultimate influence on the development of civilisation can it be regarded as in the same class with the First and Second Punic Wars. But it compares quite favourably with, for instance, Caesar's Helvetian War.

Incidentally, there is one thing I don't like about conquerors. It may be only a personal idiosyncrasy, but I feel it is an objection that should be given due weight by the historian. At heart these conquerors are not really barbarians; or, if they are, they appear to be unnecessarily hypocritical about the business. Instead of saying that their actions spring from a natural ferocity, and that they like it, they trot out the old respectable formulas about introducing a new era of justice and social reform, with the underlining of a halcyonic future of Jobs for All.

Give me the conqueror who says dispassionately, "This is a rotten world and I trust before I'm finished with it to make it a lot worse. In fact, I hope, with the help of Providence, to make this world so rotten that nobody can live in it. Not even myself." Such would truly be a great conqueror; but, alas, history has no record of him.

Another aspect of written history that is of particular interest to the student is the works dealing with strategy and statecraft. The great figures of history – how did they do it? Was it with brains or did they fluke it? Or did they possess some mystical superhuman attribute unknown to the multitude.

One recalls the other-world fascination of a saunter through the Reading Room of the British Museum as it used to be. Anaemic, bespectacled figures, poring stoop-shouldered over heavy sociological and biographical tomes, obsessed with the mirage of fame and power, seeking the key to world domination, some of them; others, reformers, aflame with a vision.

This is all very queer. What is queerer still is that a not inconsiderable percentage of these stoop-shouldered students have pulled it off.

It may quite conceivably be proved in the near future that there is no such thing as history; that it is an illusion; a fantastic by-product of man's search for the divine. But how much poorer we would be without this colourful procession. A motley crowd on the banks of the Tiber. New-painted argosies. A Phoenician haggling on an English beach. Tyre in flames. The twilight on Helen's face.

Ah, long ago . . .

Innocents Abroad

A singular circumstance with regard to my own life, that I have observed in the course of the years, is that when I have been passing through a fairly lengthy period of mental strain, so that I find myself to be badly in need of a change, then I discover that it is the people around me who are making arrangements to go on extended vacations. Not me, of course. Oh, no. And another queer thing, too, that I have noticed, is that when I am in this condition in which I sigh for a change of scene, for a little while to bask pleasantly in the sun, then through some inexplicable linking together of coincidence the reading matter that I accumulate over a weekend all deals with people on holiday. This weekend, for instance, I find myself with Mark Twain's *Innocents Abroad*. Jerome K. Jerome's *Three Men on the Bummel* and an Afrikaans translation of Silvio Pellico's *Ten Years in Prison*. Three delightfully escapist volumes, each having as theme the recording of a brief time of recess from the daily grind.

I am reading these books, of course. And I find them very interesting, of course – even after (in the case of *The Innocents Abroad*) the eleventh reading. But all the time, at the back of my mind, I am conscious of the existence of certain wicked, envious thoughts. Mark Twain, Jerome K. Jerome and Silvio Pellico had all the luck, I feel: they had, all three of them, each in a different way, been furnished on a generous scale with facilities for taking it easy.

At the present moment there are I just don't know how many people of my acquaintance who are proceeding abroad on a variety of earnest quests – relating, in the main, to the establishment of commercial ties or the pursuit of knowledge. Only a small minority make the candid admission that they are going overseas – to England or Europe, mostly – because there are certain features associated with foreign travel that are not altogether disagreeable.

A little while ago I had occasion to take leave, in Johannesburg, of a young lady with literary interests who was shortly embarking for England to study further. The passenger-list of every boat sailing from Cape Town to Southampton contains a liberal sprinkling of the names of South Africans of both sexes in this category. Sometimes it is more than a sprinkling, so that the list has got a peculiarly mottled sort of appearance that, for all its oddity, is not altogether unpleasing to the eye.

Anyway, this young lady in question, with literary interests, who was to make one of the boat-load of passengers sailing from Cape Town to Southampton on that particular week, informed me, in as casual a way as you please, that she was going to the United Kingdom.

My, I thought. There was something for you, now. Not like it was in the old days, when we used to board a boat for just plain England. No, she was proceeding to the whole of the United Kingdom. Meaning England and Scotland together, I reflected, through the Union of the Crowns, not to mention the legislative incorporation of England and Scotland in 1707. Naturally, I was impressed. A journey covering 6 000 miles of geographical distance could, I know, present certain vexatious aspects at times. But here was this young lady so utterly heedless of her personal safety as to be preparing to travel through a pretty solemn space of history as well. I only hoped that she would be cautioned in advance about that dangerous corner near the turn of the seventeenth century. It would be too bad if she got beheaded, or something, through accidental involvement in a religious or dynastic issue that could not have any deep significance for her.

I even wondered if that was, perhaps, why she had said "United Kingdom" in such reverential tones. With such devout gravity. Almost as though she had said "Kingdom Come".

Afterwards, however, when the young lady had left, it struck me that she might have said that she was going to the United Kingdom – all of it, like that and not just England, or London – merely so as to be on the safe side, in case the Union Castle liner went off its course and, instead of Southampton, docked in the Stronsay Firth, Orkney Islands, in the shoals among the Scotch mists, with the skipper none the wiser.

Yet, during all this time, while the young lady with literary interests who was going abroad was talking, there was something that I felt I had to tell her. But I never got so far, of course. For one thing, she was talking so fast about what she believed the United Kingdom to be like (this being her first visit there), that I couldn't get in more than a couple of words now and again, edgeways. For another thing, it is no use trying to teach people with literary interests anything. (Consider the very excellent advice proffered by Mark Twain under this head on page 531 of the book I am reading: it is official counsel presented free of charge to aspiring writers and is published as a sort of appendage to *The Innocents Abroad*. Written three-quarters of a century ago, it remains the most up-to-date and the most practical literary guidance that there is. And yet only a handful follow it. The rest are too proud.)

Nevertheless, if I could have got in a complete sentence, and if I thought that that young lady would pay any attention to what I had to communicate, then I would have tried to give her some sort of idea as to how far the United Kingdom really is removed from South Africa. I would have tried to make it clear to her as to why it is only in the English language that the expression, "keeping one's distance", has got currency. I mean, if you talk to a person in England, and he's at all well-bred, he'll keep you at a proper distance. And when two well-bred people (I am not talking about loafers, now), converse in the southern part of the United Kingdom (I am saying nothing about the northern part, now), each one keeping the other at a proper distance, then the space between them is considerably more than just the 6 000 miles separating Table Bay from Southampton Water.

What I am seeking to infer is that when one arrives in Southampton, having accomplished the voyage from Cape Town, one is not of necessity brought any nearer to the United Kingdom (southern part).

Some time later I realised that I was just being jealous of this girl because she was going abroad under conditions that were novel to me. Everything connected with her departure seemed to me so unorthodox. For instance, she wasn't afraid to let anybody know where she was going. And then, she spent a long time in saying goodbye to people. And she was leaving South Africa because she wished to go elsewhere, and not because she had to get out of South Africa – quick. Furthermore, she would arrive in London, eventually, because that was where she wanted to be – and not just through the circumstance of there not having been a ship for Australia when she went to make enquiries at the Cape Town docks, at night.

I can see now that what I resented was the unconventional way in which this young lady set about her trip overseas. She even left a forwarding address. The next thing, I felt, that she would do when she got to London, would be to go and visit Westminster Abbey and the Tower and the Tate Gallery and the National Gallery and the Victoria and Albert Museum, and get mistaken ideas about culture, instead of walking about in the sleet, battling for a living, with cardboard in her shoes.

But how do we know that this young lady's way of doing things, unorthodox though it appears, may not perhaps be the right way? When one is in Paris, for instance, should one not perhaps go and visit the Louvre and Notre Dame and the Madeleine? I wonder . . .

Maybe, next time I'm around there, I just will go and give those places the once-over.

Marico Revisited

A month ago I revisited the Marico Bushveld, a district in the Transvaal to which I was sent, a long time ago, as a school-teacher, and about which part of the country I have written, in the years that followed, a number of simple stories which I believe, in all modesty, are not without a certain degree of literary merit.

There were features about the Marico Bushveld that were almost too gaudy. That part of the country had been practic-ally derelict since the Boer War and the rinderpest. Many of the farms north of the Dwarsberge had been occupied little more than ten years before by farmers who had trekked into the Marico from the Northern Cape and the Western Trans-vaal. The farmers there were real Boers. I am told that I have a deep insight into the character of the Afrikaner who lives his life on the platteland. I acquired this knowledge in the Marico, where I was sent when my mind was most open to im-pressions.

Then there was the bush. Thorn trees. Withaaks and ka-meeldorings. The kremetart-boom. Swarthaak and blinkblaar and wag-'n-bietjie. Moepels and marulas. The sunbaked vlakte and the thorn tree and South Africa. Trees are more than veg-etation and more than symbols and more than pallid senti-mentality, of the order of "Woodman, spare that tree", or "Poems are made by fools like me". Nevertheless, what the oak and the ash and the cypress are to Europe, the thorn tree is to South Africa. And if laurel and myrtle and bay are for chaplet and wreath, thorns are for a crown.

The bush was populated with kudus and cows and duikers and steenbokkies and oxen and gemsbok and donkeys and occasional leopards. There were also ribbokke in the krantzes and green and brown mambas, of which hair-raising stories were told, and mules that were used to pull cars because it was an unhealthy area for horses. Mules were also used for telling hair-raising stories about.

And the sunsets in the Marico Bushveld are incredible things, heavily striped like prison bars and flamboyant like their kaffir blankets.

Then there were boreholes, hundreds of feet deep, from which water had to be pumped by hand into the cattle troughs in times of drought. And there was a Bechuana chief who had once been to London, where he had been received in audience by His Majesty, George V, a former English king; and when, on departing from Buckingham Palace, he had been questioned by the High Commissioner as to what form the conversation had taken, he had replied, very simply, this Bechuana chief, "We kings know what to discuss."

There were occasional visits from Dutch Reformed Church predikants. And a few meetings of the Dwarsberg Debatsver-eniging. And there were several local feuds. For I was to find that while the bush was of infinite extent, and the farms very many miles apart, the paths through the thorn trees were narrow.

It was to this part of the country, the northern section of the Marico Bushveld, where the Transvaal ends and the Bechu-analand Protectorate begins, that I returned for a brief visit after an absence of many years. And I found, what I should have known all along, of course, that it was the present that was haunted, and that the past was not full of ghosts. The phantoms are what you carry around with you, in your head, like you carry dreams under your arm.

And when you revisit old scenes it is yourself, as you were in the past, that you encounter, and if you are in love with your-self – as everybody should be in love with himself, since it is only in that way, as Christ pointed out, that a man can love his neighbour – then there is a sweet sadness in a meeting of this description. There is the gentle melancholy of the twilight, dark eyes in faces upturned in a trancelike pallor. And fra-grances. And thoughts like soft rain falling on old tombstones.

141

And on the train that night on my way back to the Bushveld, I came across a soldier who said to me, "As soon as I am out of this uniform I am going back to cattle-smuggling."

These words thrilled me. A number of my stories have dealt with the time-honoured Marico custom of smuggling cattle across the frontier of the Bechuanaland Protectorate. So I asked whether cattle-smuggling still went on. "More than ever," the soldier informed me. He looked out of the train window into the dark, "And I'll tell you that at this moment, as I am sitting here talking to you, there is somebody bringing in cattle through the wire."

I was very glad to hear this. I was glad to find that the only part of my stories that could have dated had not done so. It is only things indirectly connected with economics that can change. Droughts and human nature don't.

Next morning we were in Mafeking. Mafeking is outside the Transvaal. It is about twenty miles inside the borders of the Northern Cape. And to proceed to Ramoutsa, a native village in the Bechuanaland Protectorate which is the nearest point on the railway line to the part of the Groot Marico to which we wanted to go, we had first to get a permit from the immigration official in Mafeking. All this seemed very confusing, somehow. We merely wanted to travel from Johannesburg to an area in the North-Western Transvaal, and in order to get there it turned out that we had first to cross into the Cape Province, and that from the Cape we had to travel through the Bechuanaland Protectorate, which is a Crown Colony, and which you can't enter until an immigration official has first telephoned Pretoria about it.

We reached Ramoutsa late in the afternoon.

From there we travelled to the Marico by car. Within the hour we had crossed the border into the Transvaal. We were once more on the Transvaal soil, for which we were, naturally, homesick, having been exiles in foreign parts from since early morning. So the moment we crossed the barbed-wire fence separating the Bechuanaland Protectorate from the Marico we stopped the car and got out onto the veld. We said it was fine

142

to set foot on Transvaal soil once more. And we also said that while it was a good thing to travel through foreign countries, which we had been doing since six o'clock that morning, and that foreign travel had a broadening effect on the mind, we were glad that our heads had not been turned by these experiences, and that we had not permitted ourselves to be influenced by alien modes of life and thought.

We travelled on through the bush over stony paths that were little more than tracks going in between the trees and underneath their branches, the thorns tearing at the windscreen and the hood of the car in the same way as they had done years ago, when I had first visited the Marico. I was glad to find that nothing had changed.

Dusk found us in the shadow of the Dwarsberge, not far from our destination, and we came across a spot on the veld that I recognised. It was one of the stations at which the bi-weekly Government lorry from Zeerust stopped on its way up towards the Limpopo. How the lorry drivers knew that this place was a station, years ago, was through the presence of a large anthill, into the crest of which a pair of kudu antlers had been thrust. That spot had not changed. The anthill was still surmounted by what looked like that same pair of kudu horns. The station had not grown perceptibly in the intervening years. The only sign of progress was that, in addition to the horns on its summit, the anthill was further decorated with a rusty milk-can from which the bottom had been knocked out.

And so I arrived back in that part of the country to which the Transvaal Education Department in its wisdom had sent me years before. There is no other place I know that is so heavy with atmosphere, so strangely and darkly impregnated with that stuff of life that bears the authentic stamp of South Africa.

When I first went to the Marico it was in that season when the moepels were nearly ripening. And when I returned, years later, it was to find that the moepels in the Marico were beginning to ripen again.

Reminiscences

I was engaged for a couple of days last week in going through old files of newspapers and magazines, making a collection of stories which I had written over the past fifteen years.

In re-reading some of the Marico Bushveld stories that I had written as long ago as the early years of the 1930s I was surprised to find how intimate was my knowledge of life on the South African farm. I was also astonished at the extent of my familiarity with historical events (and the spirit of the times and the personalities who had figured in them) that had taken place in the ou Transvaal.

Anyway, in again persuing those stories, written long ago, I realised where all that local colour came from: I had got it from listening to the talk of elderly farmers in the Marico district who had a whole lot of information that they didn't require for themselves, any more, and that they were glad to bestow on a stranger. It was all information that was from a scientific point of view, strictly useless.

That was how I learnt all about the First and Second Boer Wars. And about the Native wars. And about the trouble, in the old days, between the Transvaal and the Orange Free State. And about the Ohrigstad Republic. And about the Stellaland Republic. If any contemporary South African historian would like some fallen-by-the-wayside information about any events in the early days of the South African Republics, I could supply him with all the facts he needs; and, what is more important, with a whole lot of surplus information outside of just facts.

I regarded them as wonderful storytellers, the old Boers who lived in the Marico district twenty years ago. Most of them had moved into that part of the Transvaal, next to the Bechuanaland Protectorate, in 1917. It was a part of the Transvaal that had remained practically uninhabited since the Anglo-Boer War. I still have very vivid recollections of the Boers who lived in the Marico in those days. I was there as a school-teacher for a little while. And I can only hope that the information I imparted to the children, in the way of reading, spelling and arithmatic, was in a minute degree as significant as the facts that were imparted to me by their parents, whom I went to visit at weekends.

I remember that there was old Oom Geel, who had been a Cape rebel and who still used to display a fragment of red-striped jersey that he had worn as a prisoner-of-war in the Bermudas.

Because he was a Cape rebel, Oom Geel said, he had been regarded by the English not as a regular prisoner-of-war but as a convict, and so he had been sent to the Bermudas instead of to St. Helena. And he said that when he returned to South Africa after the Boer War the former Free State and Transvaal burghers, who had been respectable P.O.W.'s at St. Helena, used to look on him with suspicion, as though he was going to pick their pockets, and so on, because he had worn a striped convict jersey in the Bermudas. I can still remember the laughter that invariably followed on this straight-faced statement of Oom Geel's.

Old Oom Geel had a very tall son, called At, and a shorter son, Jan, and a large number of grandchildren. And there were a family of Bekkers who lived on a farm, *Drogedal*. This farm seemed the size of a whole district.

I don't know how big the farm was, exactly, but in later years, when I was working for an educational publication in London, and I had to interview the principals of schools in the southern English counties, I remembered that we would approach Tunbridge Wells or Sevenoaks and the man who drove the car asked me, "Are we now in Sussex or in Surrey, do you think, or perhaps in Kent?" then I would think, "Oh, well, all these counties together are less than the size of the Bekkers' farm in the Marico."

And there was an Afrikaner family named Flaherty, with whom I boarded; and the old man Flaherty would regularly welcome me at breakfast with the greeting, "Die beste van die more," and it took me quite a while to realise that these words must have constituted a traditional family greeting, a literal translation of what the family's original Irish forebear, the first South African Flaherty, must have said habitually at breakfast time, "The top of the morning to you."

I must have known most of the families living in the Marico Bushveld at that particular time and some of those farmers had most interesting stories to tell, relating in a matter-of-fact way all sorts of unusual circumstances. And my mind absorbed whatever they had to relate provided that it was of a sufficiently inutilitarian order.

There was that legend of a spectre in the form of a white donkey that haunted the poort on the road to Ramoutsa. If you passed through that poort, just around midnight, then at the darkest part of the poort, near where the road skirts a clump of maroelas, you would be certain to encounter an apparition in the form of a white donkey with his front legs planted in the centre of the road. Nobody was quite certain where the hind-legs of the donkey were planted, because the lonely traveller would decide to turn back just about then. (I visited that part of the Marico again about two years ago. The clump of maroelas by the side of the Government road have been cut down, since those days. But the donkey is still there.)

Amongst hundreds of other stories I heard in the Marico was a first-hand account, by an elderly man who had been a burgher in that particular commando, of the sartorial eccentricities of a certain Boer War commandant. This commandant was very fussy about his appearance and always insisted on wearing white starched shirt-fronts and cuffs. No matter under what adverse conditions the commando was operating, in constant retreat from the enemy, fording swollen rivers under fire and negotiating barbed-wire fences between block-houses, every Monday morning was washing-day, with the burghers having to go into laager beside some spruit or dam (or a jackal hole with muddy water at the bottom) while the commandant supervised the washing and starching and ironing of his linen by the native agterryers.

146

It wasn't that he was personally over-fastidious about such things, the commandant explained. But it was necessary for the prestige of the Boer forces in the field, that a commandant shouldn't go about looking like a Bapedi.

My informant, the ex-burgher in this commando, said that he could never feel that the commandant's arguments carried any weight. Himself, he didn't care if he looked like a Bapedi, or like a M'Shangaan, or like an orang-outang, even, he said, as long as he didn't get shot. But the commandant was a capable officer, he said, and the burghers trusted him and admired him, although in their ragged clothes they would be aware of a certain sense of inferiority beside the commandant's starched magnificence: it was observed that when the commandant addressed a veld-kornet directly, giving him instructions, the veld-kornet would say, "Ja, Kommandant," and would meanwhile be standing shuffling somewhat awkwardly.

There was something fine, I thought, about the way the commandant led his force into a northern Cape village that the English had evacuated. He did it all in great style. He wore his best white shirt-front for the occasion. And he sat up very straight on his horse, riding at the head of his commando, with an occasional stray bullet still whistling down the street. And it was only when they got to the church square, in the centre of the village, that the burghers realised, from the circumstance of his shirt-front having gone limp, and not being white any longer, that their commandant would ride at their head no more.

Another of many stories that I heard in the Marico, and that was of particular interest to me, because it had to do with the building of a farmhouse (something that has always fascinated me) related to the sadism vented by a farmer on his step-daughter.

After you have laid the foundations for a house you start with the bricklaying. To make bricks you dig a hole in a place where the soil is clayey, and then shovel in river sand and pour in water, and you get the cattle to mill around in this sticky mud until it's all properly mixed.

Now, this farmer, who had subjected his stepdaughter to all sorts of brutalities for a number of years (she was now sixteen) hit on the idea of making her mill around, day after day, in the clay hole, along with the cattle, helping to tread the clay until it was of the right consistency for making bricks out of. Anyway, the point of this story is that this sixteen-year-old girl one day studied her reflection in a mirror and came to the conclusion that she was very pretty, with the result that she shortly afterwards clambered out of the clay hole where she had been tramping about in thick mud that came up to her thighs, and she ran away from the stepfather's farm to Johannesburg.

In the city, men found her desirable – as her reflection in the mirror had told her that they would do – and so she went wrong. But they say that in Johannesburg she dressed very fashionably, and that she looked ever so distinguished.

And through the years that have followed, pondering on that story, I have often pictured to myself that girl from the Marico clay hole walking the streets of Johannesburg. I can picture to myself the grace with which she walked the paved ways of the city, on high-heeled shoes. And I have wondered if the experience she gained in the clay hole did not do her a lot of good, after all . . . It seems to me a good way for a girl to acquire an elegant gait. Stepping high . . .

Thinking about the Old Marico in this way gave me a sense of nostalgia last week. I felt I wanted to hear more stories, at first hand, of the Transvaal's bygone days. It was impracticable, at the moment, to take another trip to the Marico. But I might be able to meet some old Boer, here in the streets of Johannesburg, to whom I could talk, and who, because he had seen much of life, and was a veteran of the Anglo-Boer War (and even of the First Boer War, perhaps) and had lived through stirring times in the early days of the Transvaal, would be able to discourse, at length and entertainingly, about a world that had passed away for ever. And he need not be an old Boer from Marico, either. Any elderly-looking Afrikaner, who had lived for many years on the platteland would do for my purpose.

I walked through the streets, scanning the faces of the

passers-by. But they all looked much too young. Then I saw a man lounging near a bar. He walked with a stoop. His face was lined. Many winters and summers had passed over his head: many winters, I thought. He seemed really decrepit. I invited him into the pub. Yes, he was an Afrikaner, all right. In his younger days he had lived in the Potchefstroom district. Good enough. I also knew Potchefstroom, slightly. Then he started talking. He was reminiscing, like I asked him to. But his recollection didn't seem to go as far back somehow. I wondered if his memory was perhaps beginning to fail him.

And then I asked him for his name again. And it suddenly struck me that I had met this relic from a venerable past many years before. In fact, we had been at school together, in Potchefstroom. And in the same class. And only after I had told him who I was, and had reminded him of the old days, and he had said, "Good God, I would never have recognised you. You look all gone in" – only then I realised what it is about the past that makes it seem so romantic, and I thought, eheu fugaces, I thought.

Veld Story

There is a fascination about old cemeteries of the kind that are dotted about the South African veld, family graveyards at the foot of koppies; small plots for burial grounds that were laid out during the past century, in the old days when amongst the harnesses and riems and trek-chains in the wagon-house, or by the side of the sacks of mealies in the grain shed there was always, on every farm, ready for use in emergency, a coffin.

One such old cemetery – a comparatively large one – is at Warmbaths, the headstones bearing dates going back to the 1840s. A number of Voortrekkers were buried there, not those who were leaders of any treks, but obscure persons, men and women and children, whose memories have been obliterated with the erasing of their names and the dates of their birth and death from the headstones. And when you look at the little mounds of sunbleached stones (do they search the veld specially for stones of the white sort when a mound is raised over a grave, or does the sun make the stones white with the years? – the sun and the rain?), a century does not seem so very long, somehow.

They must lie lightly on a grave, the stones that have not sunk so very deeply into the earth at the end of a hundred years.

And what is of more particular interest to a passer-by is an old cemetery somewhere on a lonely part of the veld, overgrown with tangled grass and oleanders and shut in with barbed-wire fence, the rusted strands put very close together – and all traces lost long ago of the following generations of that family that had laid its dead to rest in a piece of ground closed in with barbed wire that is clothed with half a century of rust.

Such a graveyard I came across at the weekend on a farm that is within easy reach of Johannesburg. The farm has changed hands a good number of times in recent years. The new owners, I found, did not know very much about the original family of Van Heerdens, whose names are engraved on the head-stones in the cemetery.

There is still a stretch of rising ground in the neighbourhood that is known as Van Heerden's Bult. But nobody named Van Heerden has lived in those parts for as long as most people can recall.

I could not, of course, resist the temptation to climb over that fence. The oleander – Selon's-roos it is called in Marico – at one time the most popular flowering tree in certain parts of the country, because it is hardy and stands up well to drought conditions, had grown tall and shaggy, through not having been pruned (for how long, I wondered?), but the colour of its flowers tinted in well with the yellow of the grass and the sunlight and the pallid yellow of the mood evoked by the sur-roundings, and the upper part of the graveyard reposed in the cool of the oleander's shade.

At a place where the rusted wire had sagged slightly I climbed over into the enclosure.

From force of custom I looked first at the jars that had once held flowers. As always, in a graveyard on the veld, there were a number of vases and urns, of glass and porcelain, that held a peculiar fascination because they belonged to the irrevocable past.

I have seen, on veld graveyards in the Transvaal, cut-glass vases that must have come from stately Cape homes; orna-mental earthenware vessels, graceful in shape and lovely in their colouring, of a quality and craftsmanship that has en-abled them to remain, after half a century of weathering, still without crack or blemish.

It is also a not unusual circumstance to come across, in these isolated burial places, bottles of antique design, some of them black with short necks and heavily-bellied, as though they had once contained some potent liquor, others deli-cately-shaped and in variegated patterns – made in far-off days to be receptacles of perfumes and unguents.

There were several interesting vases in this cemetery under

the oleander. There was also a green bowl of cut-glass, designed to hold fruit rather than flowers, exquisitely shaped and fitted with delicate silver handles. It had no doubt graced the sideboard of a dining-room some three-quarters of a century before. The green bowl was in superb condition, almost as though the mud with which it had been periodically splattered by one rain to be washed off by the next had also served to polish the smooth external surfaces, lingering a while in the inner curves.

On another mound were two Dresden figurines, hollowed out at the top for flowers. One of the figures was slightly chipped, but it looked good for another couple of centuries.

The names on the tombstones were all Van Heerdens, or women with other surnames who had been born Van Heerden. I looked at the dates. The last interment had taken place in the early years of the present century. It must have been after that date that the Van Heerden family had trekked away.

Then I noticed a singular circumstance. The last six or seven tombstones all bore the same date, that of a year in the early part of this century. They were all Van Heerdens. And they had all been buried between the 14th and the 30th days of September. Seven members of the family had all died within the same fortnight. The names and dates were still clearly legible. I made a closer study of the inscriptions. There were six children, three girls and three boys, the youngest eight, the oldest nineteen. And also the mother. At intervals from each other of a day or two a whole family had died and had been buried. During the month of September in a year in the early part of this century.

I wondered what had happened. How had they all come to die? It must have caused a stir in those parts, many years ago, an entire family dying off like that, within so short a period of time. It was something that must still be talked about, on winter's evenings when, the day's work done, people sat around the open fireplaces in the kitchen and talked of strange things.

I went from one farm to the next to find out how it had all

happened. And eventually I came across an old woman who had been born on a farm near where the Van Heerdens had lived. And as a young woman, who was then on the point of being married, she had attended the funerals of several of the children and of the mother. And this woman told me, simply, that the whole family had died of enteric. That was all there was to it. Just a simple story of the veld. And after that the father had trekked away. To Rustenburg, some said.

I thought, when I went away, what a wonderful theme the story of the deaths of the Van Heerdens could furnish for a novel. Each of these children and the mother. The little girl of fourteen on the threshold of womanhood, arriving at the age where she would furtively examine herself in the mirror, sloping the looking glass downwards. And the young man of nineteen, who had passed through the Sturm und Drang period of adolescence – something that would not happen to a city-bred youth for another ten years – and was already beginning to assume the responsibilities of manhood. And so with the rest of the family, with their problems and conflicts and frustrations . . . the dreams and griefs and bitterness of childhood, and the dark strugglings of adolescence. And I feel that Mrs. Van Heerden was in many ways a remarkable woman. And then all these problems suddenly solved. Just when the stage is set for the development of character, for the unwrapping of the future, for the intricacies of the unfolding of the lives of all these people – suddenly, it all stops. The story is indeed ended before it has begun. The problems are all solved before they have been fairly stated. All the loose ends tied up before they have become properly unravelled. Only life can create a story like that, so tremendous in its sweep, so intriguing in its possibilities – and so simple in the telling.

On the way back I repassed the graveyard. I also found the place where I judged the Van Heerdens' homestead had been. And some distance away was a spring, choked with gaudily-coloured weeds and long, thick grass of a brilliant green. A donga dense with all sorts of vegetation, blue lobelia and river reeds and rushes and kweekgras and yellow gazanias. And in this muddy water, slowly flowing towards the dam where there were wild ducks, must have been bred the enteric germs which half a century ago caused seven new mounds to be raised in the barbed wire enclosure beside the unpruned oleander.

Red and pink buphane also grows by the side of the donga that leads from the spring to the dam.

Paysage de la Highveld

During the past weeks I have been living on a farm on the Muldersdrift Road, thirteen miles out of town. A private bus passes this farm at six o'clock in the morning, on the way to the city. At that hour it is still dark, and it is not always easy to distinguish, from the glare of their headlights, between the bus and the farm trucks carrying agricultural produce to market. Consequently, since there are no regular bus-stops on the route, I have to describe the accepted hitch-hiker's arc with my thumb each time I see headlights. Sometimes, when I have signalled a lorry, and the vehicle happens to draw up, I get a lift as far as Newtown.

The fascination of driving along the country roads on the outskirts of Johannesburg in the early dawn has not yet begun to pall on me. And I have several times wondered why our South African artists don't paint the early morning landscape more often. When the koppies and valleys are swimming in mists. And plantations are dark masses with a soft grey light behind them. And the blurred horizons are wrapped in theology. Instead of which, our painters almost invariably limit themselves to canvases of landscape in the full glare of day or with flamboyant sunrise or sunset effects. Perhaps they leave that part of the day alone – that part of the day before the sky is red – because it is so much more difficult to catch those gris-eous tones, leaden and ashen-silver tints and neutral greens, and patches that are the colour of doves' wings; it is not just anybody that can cover a canvas with different kinds of slaty greys and still not make the thing look like a night scene. It takes a real artist to paint a landscape in dun shades – and yet to reveal it as a world filled with the morning's clean light.

It is also difficult to get that particular part of the morning on to canvas, because it is an effect that doesn't stay very long. In about ten minutes' time the sky is streaked with crimson and the magic of the grey light is gone, and you are left with the orthodox Sunrise on the Veld. Another reason why paintings of the misty pre-sunrise morning are rare in South African art is because it is hard for the South African artist to get up that early.

When I was at the Cape recently I was often made acutely unhappy, in the course of a ramble along, say, Camp's Bay beach – or, for that matter, the Muizenberg beach or Somerset Strand – through the circumstance that at every hundred yards or so I would be confronted with a typical South African artist's painting of a seascape. Azure skies and ultramarine ocean and brown rocks in the left foreground. It was all such obvious beauty . . . colour, composition, everything . . . just the sort of painting that the general public thrills to. At every hundred yards or so I was confronted by another and yet another and another picture painted by a second-rate artist.

I saw thousands and thousands of these second-rate paintings all along the Cape beaches, and they were an interminable source of distress to me. All they needed were frames. And afterwards I got so that it seemed to me that a lot of those paintings actually were framed, and some of the frames even had little red tabs on them: and one day, when I passed a large number of daubs like that, all in a row, and I found myself absent-mindedly putting my hand in my pocket for the catalogue – I knew then that I must never again take a stroll along any part of the Cape Peninsula seafront.

But it's different speeding along Transvaal highveld roads, a few miles outside of Johannesburg, by bus or farm lorry, in the dew-drenched light of a new day, before the sun is up. This is a different class of work altogether. For one thing a lot of it is water-colours; swift strokes with a full brush – as often as not flung down just apparently anyhow, on soaking wet paper, with breathtaking mastery, with the superb carelessness of certainty. And it is all early impressionism, before the impressionists became mathematicians. And just outside the Johannesburg municipal area there is a magnificent example of near Fauvism, an extraordinary piece of work, a thrilling smudge of dark trees with silver light breaking through them, against a background of blurred hills and earthy sky.

There is also an interesting painting, higher up along the Muldersdrift Road, with rows of trees and a couple of farm-houses carefully laid out in accordance with a complicated system of receding planes. But while I can admire the clever-ness of this canvas very much, it doesn't make a strong and direct emotional appeal to me. I can sense in it the beginning of the trompe l'oeil decadence of the last years of the nine-teenth century.

The last piece of early impressionism on the road comes into view at the very moment of sunrise. I can't just at the moment recall the name of this picture. And I can't make out the artist's signature, which looks like a scrawled "G" with some wrigglings after it (which makes me think that it might be Gauguin before he went to the South Seas); on the other hand, it might equally well be "S" and some scribbling after it. Seurat, perhaps? I have often wondered.

I have asked the bus driver, but he says he doesn't know.

Postscript
It is springtime on the farm. The almond trees and the apple trees, the peach and apricot and cherry trees are covered in pink and white blossom. And I, neurotic city-dweller, whom the springtimes of the last four or five years have passed by with studied nonchalance – bringing me neither enchant-ment nor rapture nor heartache – gaze upon the annual mir-acle of bursting blooms without the awakening of memories and without wonderment.

Witpoortjie Falls

About fifteen miles from Johannesburg, on the way to Krugers-dorp, is Witpoortjie, the railway halt for a natural beauty spot which for over half a century has been the regular resort of picnickers from Johannesburg and the West Rand.

Among my earliest childhood recollections is an outing to Witpoortjie in the company of my parents and some relatives and a number of friends. I remember that the party included two gentlemen with prominent cheek-bones who carried bag-pipes. I thought of, and referred to, these gentlemen as Scotch-men. It was only years later that I learnt that they were, in reality, Scots.

I was also impressed very vividly by the waterfall, which for a long time afterwards I tried to make drawings of in coloured crayons. Those were better crayons than one can get today. And I believe that those drawings, too, were better than any-thing I can do now.

And I remember also how a bottle of whisky got broken on a boulder. One of the Scotsmen broke it when he was busy pull-ing out the cork, and the whisky flowed away along the side of the boulder into the grass. My youthful mind was not able to distinguish readily, in an action in which an adult was in-volved, between accident and design. And so I thought that the gentlemen with the bagpipes had broken the bottle on purpose. What lent colour to this belief was the way in which the other gentleman with the bagpipes spoke about it, enquir-ing of his fellow-musician as to what the hell he wanted to go and do that for now.

He said many other words, also, and he spoke for a consider-able while, and it was only after everybody had had several turns at explaining to him that there were ladies present, and also children above the age of two, that he grew quieter and contented himself with kicking the crockery about that had been stacked on a white cloth spread on the grass. The cups and saucers and plates had all been piled on one spot, so that it was easy for him to kick the whole lot around without having to walk much.

I have often thought, since that picnic at Witpoortjie, that Scotsmen could also swear better in those days than they can now. In the important ways the world is not what it used to be.

The other day, in a party of three, I revisited Witpoortjie. From the railway station a footpath leads over rough ground to the foot of the two tall koppies, separated from each other by a narrow ravine that winds away through rocky fastnesses to a waterfall of not unimposing dimensions. A stream of water flows through Witpoortjie all the year round. And through the slow millenniums this stream, assisted by the elements and seasonal flood times, has eroded its course down to its present level, so that the person who treads the footpath in the deep valley between the koppies walks in the shadows of precipitous crags that have been eaten out by the quiet waters that he scoops up to make tea with.

From the station to the entrance to the poort is a walk of about thirty-five minutes. That is, it takes the holiday-maker thirty-five minutes to traverse the distance from the station to where the more exuberant scenery starts. But the return journey is different. Refreshed from a day in the open air, invigorated with the play of the wind on his body and the sun on his brow, when he strides back from the mouth of the gorge to the station the visitor to Witpoortjie rarely does the distance under three hours.

For the geologist Witpoortjie is a source of unending interest. Students from the Witwatersrand University go there every year to make notes about the rock formation. Now and again the professor in charge of the students loses his way there, and when evening comes the students make their way back to the station, alone, singing their college songs, and the professor gets rescued, a year later, by the next geological expedition from Wits.

There is one place in the poort where a colossal pile of rocks looms ominously overhead, and where the footpath leads over a mountain of debris which the eye of even the untrained geologist can identify as being the result of a recent fall. Recent, that is, geologically speaking. At all events, the debris did not seem to bear signs of more than ten thousand years of weathering. And it looked doubtful whether the overhanging crags would stay in position, like that, very long. I gave those overhanging crags another fifteen thousand years, at the outside. I went through that part of the poort quickly, geologically speaking.

It was about here, where the ravine was at its narrowest, and the road seemed all but impassable even to the pedestrian – if being a pedestrian includes wading through mud at ankle depth and clambering on all fours over boulders – it was at this stage that one of us mentioned the fact that a party of Voortrekkers had taken their wagons through Witpoortjie on their way to the Northern Transvaal. Whatever admiration I had entertained for the Voortrekkers until that moment was nothing compared with the feeling that overwhelmed me when the full import of my friend's statement sank into my consciousness. Was there nothing they did not dare, these sturdy pioneers, intrepid in their perseverance, dauntless in their faith?

No doubt they felt that the strength of their trek-chains that had not failed them over a thousand miles of veld, from the Western Province of the Cape to the Witwatersrand, would stand them in stead through Witpoortjie, also. But it must have taken each wagon about a week to get through, whereas if they had gone a couple of miles east or west they could have travelled over level veld. Indeed, they must have gone considerably out of their way to have found Witpoortjie at all.

I came to the conclusion that the Voortrekkers must have been just a shade too consciously rugged in carrying out their pioneering mission. I could not help but feel that they realised they were creating history and that it was expected of them to do it the hard way.

And viewed from the perspective of history, there is no

doubt that the Voortrekker was right. There was not much prestige about taking the short cut to the Limpopo across flat and open country. Anybody could do that. The trail of the Voortrekker had to lead through the gorges of Witpoortjie, even if it meant a detour of several hundred miles to get there.

We can imagine the look of exultation on the face of the leader of that pioneer band when the last ox-wagon, battered from its toilsome journeying over giant boulder and through muddy stream, rolled heavily on to level ground.

"That was a good piece of work, kêrels," we can hear the leader of that party of Voortrekkers saying. And it was, of course. It was a feat of pioneering courage and determination, and as such it was unforgettable. There was only one way in which they could have improved on it. They could have taken off the wheels and carried their wagons over the top of the koppie. Over the high one with the slippery sides.

Today, when you want to get to Witpoortjie Falls from the station you have to pay sixpence toll to a private landowner. This seems wrong, somehow.

But I believe there is an alternative route over the top of a koppie . . . Yes, over the high one.

Old Cape Slave Relics

The other day, in an antique shop, I saw an article of furniture that was obviously a museumpiece. It was an old Cape chair with dowellingpins less than an eighth of an inch in diameter, and the mortise and tenon joints as solid as when the chair was constructed over a century ago. I was much impressed. Then I read, on the dealer's tag attached to the chair by a comparatively new piece of string, these words, "Old Cape Slave Chair".

Well, well, I thought. Old Cape Slave Chair. Fitted with a neck-rest and side supports for the elbows, it was an ideal piece of furniture for the Old Cape Slave to relax in every morning after breakfast. This chair just showed you, all over again, that there was a certain spaciousness, a measure or refinement pleasing to good taste, about the way they lived in the Western Province about the turn of the eighteenth century. That way of life has departed for ever. And that Old Cape Slave Chair seems to epitomise, somehow, that spirit of vanished elegance, that old-world charm that has passed away.

And while musing thus on the bygone splendours of an age that enriched us with thick-walled gabled dwellings and gracious legends and hippopotamus-hide sjamboks, I felt that it would be very nice indeed if some Africana enthusiast were to retrieve from the loft of some Old Cape House a few more eighteenth century relics that would serve to remind us of our cultured past.

An Old Cape Slave Embroidered Waistcoat, for instance. There you would have something, now. The lace and gold facing would be sewn onto the brocade with long stitches: you would be able to see from the insultingly inferior quality of the needlework that those were indeed the bad old days when just about any sort of embroidered waistcoat was considered good enough for the Old Cape Slave.

And how about an Old Cape Slave Sedan Chair? That would find a place of honour in any museum. We don't use that type of conveyance any more. But I can readily conceive of what an Old Cape Slave Sedan Chair would look like. The handles would be all right, encrusted with jewels, and all that sort of thing; and they would be sumptuously padded, making it easy for the owner of the estate to carry the Old Cape Slave down to the plantation to work every day. But from the interior furnishings of the Old Cape Slave Sedan Chair you would be able to recognise the fact that those were indeed the days of slavery. There would be just a coarse horsehair cushion to sit on, and in place of a curtain a strip of undyed hessian would flutter from the window opening. All this would serve to make it clear to you as to how unenlightened that past age was really. Nothing was too good for the boss: the handles had to be jewelled and padded because they made contact with his aristocratic neck and illustrious shoulders. The Old Cape Slave had to put up with a horsehair cushion and a piece of sacking for a curtain. He simply had no status. Why, they wouldn't carry a mine-native to work today, seated on a horsehair cushion.

It is hard to keep one's temper when one reflects on some of the more disagreeable features that skulked behind the imposing facade of gentility and refinement that appeared to constitute the order of things in the Old days of the Cape.

I have made mention, in a previous article, of the keen competition in the curio and antique trade today for Old Cape prints and Old Cape fittings. We make those things no more. The factories of the post-Industrial Revolution have put an end to the highly-skilled craftsman turning out the products of his trade by hand. The machine has swept all that away. And I am pleased that Old Cape relics are today held in such high esteem.

But the Old Cape Slave has so far been somewhat neglected. And it is nice to think that he is at last coming into his own. I feel that the Old Cape Slave Chair I saw in an antique shop the other day is opening up a number of splendid and hitherto unexplored possibilities. We all know about an Old Cape Slave

Bell. There are lots of them about. More rare is the Old Cape Slave Chain. This is a formidable affair, and rather frightening. The links are solidly fashioned out of a yellowish metal, and the Old Cape Slave was even proud to wear his Chain on Sundays: it dangled cumbrously from the lower part of his Old Cape Slave Embroidered Waistcoat, the links flashing in the sun. I am sure that there are still lots of Old Cape Store souvenirs waiting to be discovered by collectors in Old Cape Lofts. An Old Cape Slave Dinner Service, for instance, should command more than passing interest. And what about an Old Cape Slave Suitcase?

I feel that a very romantic story could be woven around the Old Cape Slave Suitcase. "I have borne your arrogance and your meanness and your petty larcenies long enough," the Old Cape Slave would say to Hendrik Terreblanche, the Old Cape Slave Owner. "I have packed my suitcase, and I am off."

"But you can't do that," the eighteenth century Cape Slave Owner would answer, "Or if you must go, won't you at least stay on until the end of the month?"

"A slave does not work on a month to month basis," the Old Cape Slave would reply with icy dignity. "I have packed my suitcase and I am going. Fare you well, Simon Legree."

"But you got me all wrong," the Old Cape Slave Owner would reply. "You got me mixed up with the Southern cotton plantations. You're talking nineteenth century liberation propaganda. If you walk off like that, carrying your suitcase and all, you'll be betraying a whole epoch. Be your age, man."

Thus appealed to, in the historical realisation of the fact that the honour of an entire era was at stake, the Old Cape Slave would put down his suitcase in the shade of an Old Cape Slave Oak Tree and seizing the hand of Hendrik Terreblanche in a manly grasp, he would proclaim, "Never will I desert you. I shall never go down to history in obloquy. I would rather go in a ricksha. I refuse to walk out of the eighteenth century, carrying a suitcase. Toujours, l'esprit de corps!"

"Noblesse oblige," Hendrik Terreblanche would answer simply, the tears starting to his eyes as he crushed the Old

Cape Slave's fingers in a vice-like grip. After that he would trip up the Old Cape Slave and kick him a number of times in the stomach and ribs. And for quite a long while after that he would be jumping up and down on the Old Cape Slave's face.

Done on the stage, this should be a very moving finale, with the curtain falling to slow music. A stage play on these lines, with the title *Saving a Century*, or *The Honour of the Eighteenth*, should prove very successful, especially if some tie-up could be effected with Bradmans's eighteenth century in first-class cricket or with one of Gordon Richard's more outstanding turf triumphs.

It is possible that present-day taste may recoil somewhat from the realism of the climactic scene, on the score that while it is certainly very lifelike it errs in respect of being slightly too robust. But I think that the necessary adjustments could be made quite readily. Thus, if a company were touring the smaller towns of the Free State highveld, the more virile ending to the play, *'n Eeu van Ondergang Gered*, could be safely retained.

On the other hand, if the play is produced in amateur circles – by Form IV convent girls, for instance – at the moment when Hendrik Terreblanche and the Old Cape Slave shake hands the slave owner's little daughter could walk on to the stage with a pretty, mincing gait, and bearing, clutched in her arms, a copper eighteenth century Old Cape coal scuttle filled with assorted fruits. Tableau.

Another light touch that could also be introduced in the last scene, and that should go down well with the audience, would be to arrange, the instant the Old Cape Slave puts down the suitcase, for a couple of silver spoons, bearing Hendrik Terreblanche's monogram, to drop out.

The stage props should consist of genuine period furniture and fittings that may be had on loan from the antique dealers. All the Old Cape Slave stuff may then be trotted out. Everything from an Old Cape Slave Dinner Wagon to an Old Cape Slave Antique Cabinet.

Simian Civilisation

I came across a man recently who informed me that he had spent many years of his life in studying the habits of baboons in various parts of southern Africa. Some of the things he told me about baboons were quite new to me. With many other facts that he had to impart, however, I was already familiar. Monkeys, baboons, orang-outangs, gibbons, apes, gorillas and the various other members of the simian race (including that wonderful little creature, the nagapie), have always fascinated me. I have never been able to view a monkey's drolleries in any spirit other than that of a high seriousness – which I have not always, alas, been able to accord to the loftiest and most portentous products of the human mind.

I have come to the conclusion, regrettably enough, that I have a great deal in common with the more inferior class of monkey, the kind of monkey who, through an unhappy degeneracy of spirit, is not able to approach the more solemn things of life with a proper sense of gravity. I have noticed that I get awed by the same sort of thing that a monkey does: a bee flying upside down, for instance – I saw one only the other day, and I was terror-stricken. If I didn't immediately get a witness to confirm that what I saw really was so, I wouldn't be here today, penning this sage thesis. But the witness, who has a calm and detached sort of mind, bordering on the scientific, said, yes, it was quite all right. Under certain conditions bees were known to fly sort of half sideways, for short distances. There was a natural science reason for it, too. Something to do with pollen, my witness said. Or with beeswax. Or bees' knees. I forget which. But this explanation relieved my mind all right. I thought that the bee was flying that way on purpose to frighten the guts out of me. And I know that a monkey would have thought the same if he had seen a bee flying at that singular angle.

And I have noticed that I get moved to mirth by just about the same things that stimulate a monkey's risibilities. Only, the monkey has got a more subtle sense of humour than I have, and sort of more refined. This latter circumstance has been communicated to me at intervals by people who, having been misled by the titles, have at various times read some of my writings under the impression that I had something instructive to impart.

Anyway, my informant – the one who told me about baboons – said that he had studied these creatures from the Cape to the Zambesi and beyond, and also from the Kalahari desert to Moçambique. I need not stress the patriotic thrill I derived from this demarcation, in terms of geographical area. Whatever flags fly over these regions, and in whichever way they are divided up into spheres of political influence, all the territory enclosed within the above boundaries I regard as part of my homeland, part of my native soil. And it was with a warm surge of patriotic pride that I learnt that, in going to look for baboons whose ways he could study at close hand, my informant did not find it necessary to proceed beyond the borders of my own, my native land. He didn't go and look for baboons in Belgium. No. Or in Bulgaria. No. He knew the best boys in the game were all here.

Incidentally, my informant disclosed to me that in the Kalahari his study of baboon life was somewhat complicated by the presence of Bushmen. He said that he would often, for days on end, be studying, through the binoculars, the behaviour of a clan of baboons, and he would discover only afterwards, when he had wasted a lot of time, that he had merely been observing the antics of a troop of Bushmen. And because he was much in earnest about his studies, it annoyed him to have, on occasion, to draw his pencil through many pages of notes that he had compiled on what he had taken to be an unusually primitive assemblage of baboons, only to learn that he had in reality been watching a tribe of blue-stomach (bloupens) Bushmen.

He said that on one occasion, when he complained to the chief of a Bushman tribe about this matter, the chief was very sympathetic. He said that the chief made it clear that the tribe of Bushmen had been aware for many weeks that a white man was watching them, and that they had feared that from that distance he might come to a mistaken conclusion about them. The Bushman chief also admitted that, taken by and large, the average Kalahari baboon was more advanced, from the point of view of civilised accomplishments, than the average Kalahari Bushman. But that wasn't because the baboon had a better brain than the Bushman, the chief explained. It was only because the Bushman lived deeper in the Kalahari, and therefore did not have the same opportunities for becoming civilised as what the baboon enjoyed.

Nevertheless, there were certain fields of activity in which the Bushman would always be able to more than hold his own in competition with the baboon, the chief declared. "Like when it comes to turning up a scorpion from underneath a stone," he said. "A Bushman is much quicker than a baboon at pulling off the scorpion's tail, before he can get stung, and then popping the rest of the scorpion into his mouth and eating it up. You will see that in that part of the Kalahari where there are scorpions the Bushman is always faster than the baboon."

So much for what my informant communicated to me of his general impressions of life in the Kalahari. I have recorded his observations merely for their ethnological value. But when he went on to announce that he had made a detailed study of the language of the baboons – then I really was interested.

Language of any description fascinates me. The sound of a word can drive me mad – if it's the right word: and then I don't care in what language it is spoken, or even if it is a word that somebody has made up. Speech. The eternal grandeur of sentences, even if you don't know their meaning. Many years ago I made up the word "mokador" – signifying the feeling of exaltation you get, of ecstatic elation, when a word is used correctly. And the word mokador, used in this sense, even got so far as to gain a limited currency among my more intimate associates.

And then, one day, when I was on a Union Castle boat, and we were somewhere between Madeira and North Africa (it was wartime and the ship was taking an unusual course, the captain being apparently more concerned about torpedoes than reefs) and then to larboard there looked like what was land on the horizon, and I asked a deck-hand what it was, and he answered, "That is the Mokador coast." And until this day I don't know whether there really is such a part of the globe, or whether the Mokador coast only means clouds on the horizon that look like land. Anyway, I want to go there . . .

And so, when my informant spoke about baboon talk, he got me. The magic of trailing participles. The wonder of finding yourself completely shut in by an adjectival clause, so that you have got to climb right over it, like over a galvanised iron fence, in order to get on with the next thing you want to say. Swimming through waves and floating in air and leaping across chasms. Doing with sentences the things you can't do in actual life: or that you can do only rarely.

Mind you, I have also watched baboons on krantzes, and I have listened to what they have had to say, but I have been able to follow only their simpler comments. When the patriarch of a troop comes down the krantz, for instance, a good distance in advance of the rest of the baboons and in the general direction of the mealie-field, and he pauses to examine the lay of the land – then I know that when a juvenile voice from the troop calls out, "Ee-ee ah-ee eeh," it means "It's O.K. Go ahead. Don't be a sap all your life."

Ordinary baboon conversation of that description I can understand quite easily. When a baboon comes across the old trap of a calabash containing peanuts, with the opening large enough for him to insert his empty hand, but too small to enable him to withdraw his peanut-filled fist, I am always baffled by the words the baboon uses then, when he saunters past the calabash with an air of scornful derision. "Huh-uh, Uh-huh," he says, and sometimes also "Hah-hah." But I have never been able to understand what those words mean.

My informant assures me that he had great difficulty in mastering the intricacies of baboon grammar, more especially as there are no reliable textbooks on the subject available. He says that his enquiries at some of the better class Johannesburg book-sellers produced little more than polite stares. That just shows you. If he had asked for French or Spanish, or even German or Esperanto, they would have been able to supply him. But because it is South African, they think it isn't done, or something.

Another obstacle which my informant encountered in his philological studies is the fact that there are so many different dialects. The nearest to where they talk standard baboon, he said, is along the Dwarsberge, in the Northern Marico bush-veld. Incidentally, he says that the worst baboon grammar he came across was in the coastal strip north of Lourenço Marques. The double suffix employed by the baboons of this area, in the genitive plural, sounded almost distressingly inelegant. He could only attribute it to Colonial Portuguese influence, he said. Nevertheless, as the result of patient study and research carried on through the years, my friend claims to have acquired a fair mastery of the baboon language.

"But when I talk to them, they can still detect that I am a foreigner," he explained, modestly. "They can tell by my accent, and because I haven't got hair on the top part of my feet."

Finally, and purely as a matter of interest, I asked my informant:

"What words does a baboon use in describing a human being?"

He hung his head.

"I would rather not answer that one," he said. "You see, there are some words too low – too discreditable – too defiling – to be translated in terms of any vocabulary."

A Bushveld Film Comedy

Under the heading, "Outstanding Film Previews I have Attended" I would have no hesitation in placing the Press showing of Unifilms' full-length fiction feature film *Die Wildsboudjie* high on the list.

In London I remember Charlie Chaplin's *Modern Times*, which had received so much advance publicity that by the time it was exhibited to the Press the events connected with the actual showing were more in the nature of a stampede than a preview. First, there was the rush to get in. Then there was the rush to get out, back to Fleet Street to turn out copy in time for the afternoon papers.

Even elderly journalists who had not left their sub-editorial desks for years (and had stolen the regular film critics' tickets to attend the show) displayed surprising agility in surmounting obstacles. It was certain that only one man retained sufficient presence of mind to have a quick one, first, in the Strand.

It is sad to think that this film, after all that fuss, is just about forgotten.

And then there was the preview of a French film shown in the Academy Theatre, and no less than three write-ups, in different newspapers, began with the words "I have seen it!" I wish I could remember the name of that film today.

But the showing of *Die Wildsboudjie* to the Johannesburg Press at the Unifilms Studio in Berea, some evening last month, had about it certain features that were of unique interest.

In the first place, a well-stocked cocktail bar was an excellent idea. Then the film wasn't quite ready to go through the projector, with the result that during the period of waiting the bar received a measure of patronage which went a long way towards getting the audience into the right mood for appreciating a Bushveld film comedy in which a great deal of play is made of the addiction of one of the characters to maroela mampoer.

The actual showing of the film was marked by a couple of well-timed interruptions through the projector getting stuck – enabling the audience once more to find its way under cover of darkness to the place under the stairs where the cocktail bar was situated.

It was a cheerful audience comprising quite a number of Johannesburg journalistic stand-bys over the past decade or so, and also a large sprinkling of people whom I didn't know because they had been imported in recent years from Stellenbosch. One of these was a woman with a passion for dogs who told me that South African police dogs are world-famous and are trained unilingually in Afrikaans because Afrikaans, with its clipped consonants and strong vowels, lends itself more readily than does English to the sharp ejaculation of commands like "Kom!" or "Sa!" or "Byt hom!"

But I felt that if I was a police dog there would be advantages, also, in being ordered about in a language that wasn't so full of crisp sounds. If the trainer spoke in well-modulated Oxford accents, I felt that it would not be so much of a strain on my nerves if I was requested to tear a fugitive's gizzard out.

As for the film *Die Wildsboudjie*, which was directed by Arthur Bennett and Louis Knobel and produced by Frances Coley, I can regard it only as representing a highly significant contribution to South African culture.

In the making of the picture there was a great deal that they fluked right. There was much in it of the authentic spirit of the platteland. The characters were living people. The humour was slow and earthy, and it was full of a heavy kind of grace, like a thorn tree standing halfway in sunshine and shadow.

The total effect which the film produced on me, after the light went on and the audience began to leave the studio, was a feeling of wistful tenderness. It was as though I had been present at the showing not of the first film I had seen in Afrikaans but at the last.

There was my recollection of the finely-acted scene when

Jan Jourdaan as Oom Abel takes the predikant (Tienie Stigh-ling) aside and explains that he will not allow a man of religion to take part in a massive piece of lying which he describes, in the splendid meiosis of the backveld, as "net so by die lieg omdraai". And I remembered all that natural charm with which scene after scene of the film was invested. And I did not mind that Frederik Burgers as Doors Visagie over-acted his role and through rather pointless clowning produced a mirth-less form of farce in place of comedy.

And in their enthusiasm to obtain strong lighting effects those who made the film succeeded, throughout several scenes, only in blotting out Hansie Hendrikz's face with light.

These were all secondary blemishes, compared with the mis-takes that they did not make. There were so many obvious pitfalls in respect of direction, production, photography, sce-nario-writing and the rest that were avoided in this film. For instance, they could have brought along a slick director from Hollywood to speed up the whole thing. There would have been more laughs in the picture, in that case. It would have been a more clever and more sophisticated sort of production all round. And the spirit of the old Bushveld would not have been in it any more.

From the point of view of art it was right here, in its utter naturalness, in its very gaucheries, even, that *Die Wildsboudjie* scored its greatest success. I could only hope that it would be a historic triumph, and that it would set the tone for future films to be made in Afrikaans. The producers do not try to compete with Hollywood.

Die Wildsboudjie is a film that could easily have fallen be-tween two stools. It could easily have sought to present the Bushveld story with a sleight-of-hand mastery for which we jolly well know we haven't got the human or technical equip-ment. Instead the finesse that went into the turning out of *Die Wildsboudjie* was of an easy sort. There was a lot of verve in it, and vivacity, and that nimbleness of mind that an old Ma-rico Boer has got, sitting on his front stoep scheming out a project for smuggling cattle across the Protectorate Border.

And what I am afraid of is that in the making of Afrikaans films in the months and years to come our film companies will think that they know better, and that they will not be content merely to strive for a wider and deeper perfection in giving shape to the vision that is an authentic part of the cultural spirit of Africa, but they will strive to emulate the Americans to the extent of turning out a second-rate Hollywood product, and they will seek to outdo Europe, pathetically trying to meet the world's masters of inner subtleties on their own ground.

This is what I fear in respect of Afrikaans films of the future. I have seen so much of it in other branches of present-day Afrikaans cultural development. But it was a mistake that wasn't made in respect of *Die Wildsboudjie*. That fact holds out a great deal of promise. It is my earnest hope that it may be fulfilled.

Now I regard Jan ("Men-of-the-world-smoke-Max") Jourdaan as a real discovery. I don't know if it is that he had a particular liking for the part of Abel Potgieter. But he has taken to film acting like a duck to water. Into some of the thinner patches of the story his work and personality introduced just that degree of vigour and animation which made the whole picture cohere.

M.S. ("Peswolk") Du Buson was first-rate as Oom Sarel, especially in the scene in which he was engaged in altercations with Jan Jourdaan. These two actors supported each other well. They should be very attractive team-mates in future films.

The two girls in the picture, Hansie Hendrikz as Elsa and Frances Fuchs as Lettie, did rather less than justice to the admittedly slight roles allotted to them. There was not much to choose between them. Certainly neither shone.

Antonius Ferreira was adequate in the part of the romantic konstabel. Nevertheless, an attempt at infusing a little more life into his role would not have come amiss. As for Emgee Pretorius (Wynand Potgieter), if he had been cut out of the film altogether, I hardly think anybody would have noticed.

Tienie Stighling as a predikant was good only in a negative sense. He had the superlative dignity that the role calls for. But he did not have the necessary resilience to portray the amazing subtleties that reside in the character of the backveld predikant. It was apparent to me, also, that the scriptwriter, Ina Albertyn, in her adaptation of the dialogue for screening purposes did not always succeed in conveying the brilliance of the stage play by Fritz Steyn. This is probably another reason why the predikant did not emerge completely as a man with two distinct personalities: as a human being and as a pillar of the church. (It is because of this conflict that goes on inside him all the time that the predikant as a character is so beloved of every writer.)

Die Wildsboudjie was a good show. I paid a visit to the Northern Transvaal Bushveld a couple of weeks ago, partly in order to recapture some of the atmosphere. Local colour and all that sort of thing. And then I realised where, as a sound film, Die Wildsboudjie falls down. The picture does not make enough of Nature's noises. Maybe as Francis Thompson says, Nature speaks in silence. At all events, in Die Wildsboudjie shots of the Rustenburg bushveld, the voice of the tortelduif is mute.

South African Slang

An announcement which helped to liven up the columns of the South African Press was that little item about the request made by Mr. Eric Partridge, the world-famous compiler of slang dictionaries, for South African slang words. The fascination that the real, living slang term has for Mr. Partridge is understandable. Slang, if it is alive, is the twin brother to poetry. The rejected vernacular of today, if it is vital enough, becomes part of tomorrow's polished prose. All this we know.

Now a couple of Cape Town detectives have dug up (according to the *Rand Daily Mail*) a handful of words and expressions that form part of our South African prison argot. So far so good. I trust Mr. Partridge will find colloquialisms like "lawaaiwater", "poegaai" and "Goewerment's hond" useful. But I strongly advise him to reject the claim put forward by these two detectives to the effect that a criminal – to quote the *Rand Daily Mail* report – "always refers to the detective who handled him as 'my king'."

I can understand the two Cape Town detectives in their interview with the *Rand Daily Mail* correspondent, working in a quick one like that, in order to put up their own prestige. We all know that detectives are very smart, and bright on the uptake. But I have still to meet the crook who refers to the "john" who pinched him as anything else but a lousy, motherless bastard. (And, a whole lot of other quite unprintable words besides.) All these things are merely by the way. Crooks will have their little jokes, and so will detectives.

But Eric Partridge, in appealing for authentic examples of words and phrases pertaining to this country's underworld, has embarked on a very serious quest. Living slang is the true basis of great literature.

I have a bone to pick with the writer of a sub-leader in the same issue of the *Rand Daily Mail*. This writer says, "English-speaking criminals in this country almost certainly take their cue from that great Alma Mater, the East End of London; while their Afrikaans-speaking colleagues probably rely on the vocabulary of District Six." These two statements are not altogether inaccurate. The elements mentioned by the writer are strongly represented in South African prison jargon.

But we have a specifically South African prison slang, also, that does not derive exclusively from Dartmoor and Pentonville, and that has not sprung entirely from within the narrow confines of District Six and Roeland Street Gaol. And what of the important contributions made by our Bantu criminals? What of words like "fokkies", and "stokkies" and "unsagu"? All living words of organic growth in the criminal parlance of this country.

Insofar as the European section of the community is concerned, the great clearing house for crime and criminals, during the past few generations, has been the Pretoria Central Prison.

And the first English-speaking criminals of any note who were incarcerated in the Pretoria Central Prison, in the early years of this century, were not hearts-of-oak from Britain, or English-speaking South Africans, but Australian gangsters from Australia. These Australian gangsters were big noises in the South African underworld in the early part of the present century, and the traditions they established will, of necessity, die hard. No place in the world is as conservative as a prison. And from the point of view of old-world conservatism the Pretoria Central Prison cedes place to none.

Naturally, the language employed by these Australian crooks was good Australian – a language reaching back to the deportation hulks of the pre-Victorian era. So what these Australian gangsters in South Africa spoke, when the Central Prison was in its infancy, was nineteenth century English prison slang, enriched with the salty tang of a specifically antipodean robustness. These Australian gangsters – they are nearly all dead, now, alas: hanged, most of them – laid the foundation for the English-speaking part of South Africa's prison traditions. Indirectly, they affected the Afrikaans-speaking part, also.

Anyway, the superlatives in most common use in the Pretoria Central Prison are "rhybuck", "bosker", "bonza". Ain't they all Australian words? They are used in expressions like "This is rhybuck Swaziland dagga," or "a bosker pair of New York cities," or "The judge only hit me for ten years: which was bonza, seeing as how I was expecting the rope." And so on. Yes, that's bonza. And one also hears several of these superlatives joined together, like in "she was a rhybuck bosker moll." (I need not expatiate on the world of melancholy and pathos implicit in the use of the past tense, "was". Where is the same moll today?)

"Rhyming slang" is, of course, pure East End. And the Central Prison is full of it. "Cheese-and-kisses" for missus; "pot of glue" for screw (meaning "warder"); "bees and honey" for money; "bees-knees" for – I forget for what now; "dickey-dirt" for shirt; "armour-rocks" for socks. And so on, to infinity.

The Afrikaners have contributed a set of colloquialisms that is intrinsically their own. Alas, they refer, in most cases, to dagga-smoking or burglary.

But so much for extraneous influences. Let us get down to witnessing a parade of some of the battered shibboleths of South Africa's underworld, not bothering our heads any further as to where these expressions come from.

All right, we know for a start that a detective is a john. (Quite an important start, too, by the way: if it wasn't for the johns there wouldn't be nobody in boob.) Yes, that's right. The word in most common use in South Africa for a gaol or a prison is the word "boob". "How long have you been in boob?" "We tame lions in this boob." "The last time I done boob was for rape." "Porridge Joe ain't just an ordinary convict: he is a boob-head." The expression "cold stone jug", for the Pretoria Central Prison, is used also, but rarely.

The cell is known as a "peter", or a "pozzy". Serving a sentence is "doing time". And "time" is once again divided into its component parts. (A feat Einstein couldn't perform.) Anyway, "doing time" is divided up as follows: if you are doing from six months to two years, it is called "a sleep"; from two to four years it is known as "a cut"; anything over four years is "a stretch". Thus you hear scraps of conversation like, "it was just after I done my cut; just before I landed my stretch".

In the *Rand Daily Mail* article the writer makes reference to a "nark". But in South Africa the word "nark" is not employed in its English sense. With us, the word is used purely in the sense of a squeaker. It means a man who comes his guts to the johns on his one-and-eights; who bleats on his pals; in other words, who goes and puts another man's pot on with the screws. In brief, a shelf. Somebody that snitches.

A practice indulged in by every unregenerate South African criminal – white, native, coloured or Indian – is that of dagga ("boom") smoking, and I recommend it to Mr. Partridge's notice. (Not the practice of smoking it, of course, but the word for it.) Boom is the most common word for the narcotic weed that is known as Indian hemp, or, scientifically, as cannabis Indica, and that is smoked by the criminal classes of all the above-mentioned races in this country, including the Portuguese. Another word for boom is "Nellie". Or "slaai". Or "American Navy-cut". Or "the queer". But it is all dagga in the end. By the way, "the queer," meaning dagga, must not be confused with the other term, "the very queer" – signifying methylated spirits. (I suppose these two names in prison jargon, for dagga or methylated spirits, respectively, are not entirely unrelated to the effects produced by "the queer" and its stalwart companion, "the very queer".)

A shameful circumstance in regard to the South African Prison patois is the fact – I hesitate to say it – that a large proportion of its working-day vocabulary is not unconnected with the cruder forms of house-breaking and theft. The expression "working-day vocabulary", is particularly apposite if we remember that any piece of active crime is referred to as a "job", and therefore embraces house-breaking, store-breaking, safe-blowing, bank robbery under arms. It is all grist to the mill.

When a gang does a job inside, one man has to watch in the street. He is known as the "long-stall". It is the long-stall's duty to give his pals the office when a john comes along, or when somebody starts drawing crabs; in other words, when some unauthorised busy-body, without knowing what is afoot, commences, either in ignorance or through malice, to make the lay hook. (Or crook, one also says. Or onkus.)

Sometimes, after the job is done, the rest of the gang split the swag fairly with the long-stall. But mostly they work a roughie on him. If the point they show him is of only small dimensions, then it means that the rest of the gang only "put in a weed"; but if they cut him up badly, then they "lashed". Thus, you hear a man bleating in this strain, "I won't take a snout to you blokes putting in a weed, but this is lashing. Understand, it is lashing."

I have been afforded exceptional facilities for studying South African prison slang at first hand, and rather extensively. And I believe that in this tarnished word currency, which strictly illumines the mode of life of a little-known and rather terrible world, we have something that comes very near to the earthy side of real poetry. It is something that has genuine literary significance: the fact that a few rough and sullied words can lay bare the whole inner life of a criminal, and make a prison up in a moment, with its gates and walls and warders, in sunshine and in shadow.

Christmas Celebrations

The Feast of the Nativity has certain attributes in respect of spiritual and emotional content, in respect of a lot of human beings being jolly together, that gives it a worthy place alongside of the old pagan festival from which – according to no less an authority than the late General Booth – it was, presumably, derived.

Any student of ancient history, any classics scholar, any person who has studied the rise of the Christian Church, will tell you that the ancients had their saturnalias and wassails and Priapic orgies – jolly junketings – wanton merrymakings – Sybaritic carousals, that were well established local institutions long before the monks came along to convert the peoples of Western Europe to Christianity, and that the wildest feasts of all, those associated with the equinox, with the winter solstice, the coming back of the sun, were incorporated into practices of the Christian Church.

The priests saw that they wouldn't have a hope of converting the pagan peoples to Christianity if they tried to take away from them their religious revelries that had existed from of yore. As G. K. Chesterton has pointed out, a holy-day for God had to become a holiday for man.

And in the Christian World there isn't a holiday that can compare with Christmas.

Luther achieved a queer thing with his Reformation, however.

I have noticed that differences exist between the way in which Christmas is celebrated in predominantly Catholic countries as contrasted with what is customary in predominantly Protestant countries. Among nations strongly under the influence of the doctrines of Huss and Knox and Calvin the festival binds up with the longest winter's night – celebrating, from a-far off, the coming of a new spring, with the days no longer "drawing in" – and has had its accents removed from the feast of the Nativity to what is chronologically the first day of the New Year in terms of the Gregorian Calendar.

Amongst the Afrikaners, for instance, Christmas is the holy day, New Year's Day the holiday. It is the same in Scotland. The ritual of the first-footing. A happy band carrying bottles of whisky. The first knock at the door announces the passing of the old year and the birth of the new. And to make it lucky the first man to cross the threshold must be dark. For many years I thought that I was the only person to resent this institution. But some time ago a Scotsman of my acquaintance told me that he felt more bitter than I did about what he called a barbarous piece of superstition. This Scotman's nickname, incidentally, was "Carrotty" – insofar as the world at large was concerned. Only to his intimates was he known as Ginger.

People do a lot of queer things at Christmas time that they, quite possibly, wouldn't do on just an ordinary weekday.

For instance, in Paris, they have the Cup of Noël. I dare say lots of people haven't heard of this cup event. It is a contest arranged for les nageurs. Anybody who wants to can enter for this competition, whether he can swim or not. The organisers don't care.

Briefly, this Noël Cup event consists in the entrants taking part in a swimming race across a reasonably wide part of the Seine on Christmas day.

That's all there is to it.

The last time I was present at this annual swimming contest – in the capacity of a spectator, not of a nageur – was in the middle of what was known as a hard winter. The snow on the pavement was hard and slippery and had a dirty colour. The traffic cops in the Paris streets were standing on three-foot high platforms ingeniously constructed out of ice – which did not melt on account of the temperature having been, for days, considerably below freezing point. The hot drink vendors shivered in front of the charcoal braziers in their little carts. The charge for admission to the raft from which the swimmers took to the water was ten francs.

It was worth more than ten times that sum, the fun you got

out of watching the contestants sitting shivering in their gaily striped costumes waiting for the starter's pistol. The starter knew that the members of the public were enjoying themselves. He hesitated several times before firing the pistol. Maybe he hoped that if he feinted a couple of times there would be a false start and that such of the entrants who dived into the Seine would have to be fished out again, to take their places on the edge of the raft all over again. But that didn't happen. Perhaps, the swimmers were wise to the starter's tactics. Anyway, when the pistol shot rang out they all got away in good style. There were several women amongst them. How they fared nobody seemed to worry about very much. When the swimmers had got so far towards the other bank of the Seine you couldn't see their struggles in the cold water very clearly, the members of the public who had paid ten francs to see the beginning of the race walked off the raft and went home. They didn't wait to hear the judge's decision. It didn't matter very much who won. The spectators weren't interested. For the public it sufficed that there should be over two dozen people again, this year, mad enough to jump into the Seine when it was cold. And on Noël, too, of all days.

On another occasion, on December 25th, I witnessed what I thought was a rather unusual species of frolickings. It was near a little place called Rosendael, somewhere between Dunkirk and the Belgian border. I believe they call this part of the country French Flanders. At all events, the street names in the villages have nearly all got Flemish names, and it is not unusual for a store keeper to address one in Flemish rather than in French.

The narrow streets twisted a good deal, and the little houses are covered all round, on the outside, with wooden shutters, like a sort of Venetian blind. Many of the walls are placarded with a notice proclaiming it an offence to carry on in a certain fashion: forbidding something that one feels only a lunatic would try and do. Anyway, the way of life of the natives there seems as strange as anything one would encounter in, say, the Thabazimbi area, before the mining of base metals started up.

And so when, early on Christmas morning, I saw about a score of women doing some sort of a folk dance in a village street – a somewhat ungraceful kind of a dance, in which the performers kept their arms lightly folded across their bosoms and seemed to move their feet only for the purpose of maintaining their balance on the cobbled street – I felt that this was merely another local custom, a traditional mode of welcoming the anniversary of the day of Christ's Nativity.

I said to a man that I thought it was a pretty ceremony, it being a matter for regret, only, that the women wore that peculiar kind of costume (national or local or peasant – I didn't know) because it made them look so fat. But it was nevertheless an attractive way of celebrating Christmas, I said.

The man I spoke to seemed contemptuous of my ignorance. His attitude was that only a stranger could be so unenlightened as to assume that merely because the birthday of the local hero or saint should have fallen, by coincidence, on the 25th day of December, it followed for that reason that the dance in the village street was connected with Christ's Nativity.

They knew that today was Noël, of course, the man informed me. And they celebrated Christmas Day. But naturally. The villagers were not so far behind the times as not to know that December 25th was Christmas Day. But the place was en fete for a local patron or saint (or hero or demigod or bully or hermit – I didn't know which) and it was only awkward that he should also have been born on December 25th. Surely, it was a matter not difficult to comprehend. Only in the mind of a stranger could there be any confusion about it.

But the place in the world where I have been most conscious of the feelings of open-hearted gaiety that are associated with Christmas has been Johannesburg. And it is a sad thought for me that Christmas in Johannesburg isn't what it used to be. The old days when we all walked the streets on Christmas Eve, hilariously, wearing paper caps and flickering all passers-by with coloured plumes and calling out greetings. And the area between the Law Courts and the Town Hall and between President and Kerk Streets was closed to wheeled traffic.

And everybody was in a good mood. Young men and girls. Parents with their children. Old-timers of Johannesburg, staggering in and out of pubs. The spirit of a great joy and a godlike laughter in the air.

Those old Christmas Eves when the pavements were gaudy with romance. The city of Johannesburg seems to be less innocent than it was in those days. And so are we, too, apparently.

Johannesburg Riots

The other evening I took a quiet stroll down Market Street in the direction of the City Hall, where a meeting to be addressed by Dr. Malan was scheduled to be held.

I passed the old Post Office and turned into President Street. The approaches to the City Hall were blocked by large crowds over whom a strange sort of hush seemed to have fallen – an unusual sort of quiet that deepened as I threaded my way through the multitude. And because I had spent a number of years away from Johannesburg, I did not immediately detect the underlying significance of that hush. I was deceived by that air of outward tranquillity. Because of the years during which I had absented myself from Johannesburg I had forgotten the signs. Momentarily. I had forgotten that in this city a hush of that description is always pregnant with great potentialities. That atmosphere of outward tranquillity is Johannesburg before a storm.

When I had got to about a hundred yards from the main entrance of the City Hall the crowds of soldiers and civilians had thinned. Instead, I was confronted by a long line of police constables who were strung along the pavement, under those trees that always look unmistakably like Africa in the misty light of the streetlamps, and across the street. I edged along the while and took up my stand to the right of the policeman on the end of the line. I addressed him. I informed him that I was a journalist and that I wished to attend the meeting in the City Hall. The policeman did not answer me. So I spoke again, this time in Afrikaans.

"Ek is 'n koerantman," I said to him. And I explained that I wanted to go to the meeting.

Still I received no answer. Instead the policeman, patterning himself after his colleagues in this long extended line, proceeded to bend himself double. It was a queer sort of a posture and I was struck with its unusualness. There were about a hundred policemen in that part of President Street, and they were all doing the same thing. They stood bent forward, with their heads somewhere below the level of their knees and the posterior portions of their bodies raised skywards. It was a position that, whatever else might have been said about it, I could not describe as dignified. You know what I mean. A policeman has got such a long sort of body, and when it is bent double in that fashion the effect is, to a high degree, mirth-provoking.

I also noticed that the policeman whom I was addressing and from whom I was getting no reply, had taken off his helmet and was grasping it firmly in both hands, holding it in such a way that its tall crown and wide brim covered his face and head and a portion of his stomach as well. By this time the stillness was unbearable. If the policeman had answered me, I would have become hysterical.

But the next moment I understood everything. A shower of bottles and half-bricks and pieces of masonry hurtled out of the eerie shadows of the trees in President Street and thundered against the policemen's helmets. I breathed a sigh of relief. It was only the spirit of Johannesburg once more asserting itself. The undying spirit of the mining town, born of large freedoms and given to flamboyant forms of expression.

In that moment I realised that Joh'burg had not changed. If you know Joh'burg, the sound of a half-brick rattling against a policeman's helmet tells you everything. I sensed that I had arrived in front of the City Hall at some sort of Interval. The interval between the second fusillade of bottles and brickbats and the third baton charge.

I knew what the next move was, also. So I started running. With one hand on the back of my head. In a few moments I was one of the large crowd of men and women who were also running, and in more or less the same fashion. Except that some people held both hands on their heads as they ran.

In the course of the next hour I made only inconsiderable progress towards the main door of the City Hall. I at no time got to much more than half a stone's throw of the door before a lot of helmets got dented again and I had to put my hand up to my head and run towards the Post Office.

But eventually, in the course of some sort of diversion about the details of which nobody seemed to be very clear, I got caught up into a small crowd that became isolated from the main mob and was swept up the steps right against the glass doors of the City Hall. I pushed in through one of the doors and I was glad that I was wearing an old suit – in which I once fell off a tramcar – because as I went in a number of young men in white shirts started playing a hose into the street, soaking my trouser legs in the process. As I went in another young man, standing on top of the ticket office lunged at me with a lump of wood, missing me by a good bit and nearly toppling off his perch, at the same time.

What I am going to describe now all took place in the main lobby of the City Hall and in the passage at the side of the Hall. I never got into the City Hall to hear Dr. Malan. In spite of the efforts I made.

The front lobby swarmed with men armed with sticks, staves, chair legs, sjamboks and bicycle chains. They appeared to be in charge of a man whose name I don't know, but who wore very long sideboards.

"Get yourself a piece of chair," Sideboards said to me, a few moments after the man in the white shirt had missed me with the lump of wood. "And hurry up."

From his tone I gathered that Sideboards was a man you couldn't argue with.

So I merely asked him where I could get a "stuk stoel". Because everything that bore even the remotest resemblance to a weapon had already been grabbed up by the crowd in the lobby.

During all this time there was pandemonium going on in the street. I sensed that there would have been pandemonium in the lobby as well, if it wasn't that the rest of the men there stood in about the same degree of awe of Sideboards as I did. He kept on shouting orders which were drowned periodically by the sound of splintering glass as a half-brick thudded through the door. Every time a missile crashed into the lobby I entertained the malicious hope that it would get Sideboards on the head. Only afterwards it occurred to me that Sideboards had probably been struck on the head by a stone right at the beginning of the proceedings and that had made him so peculiar.

In the long passage next to the City Hall were a number of tables on which policemen were reclining. Some of them seemed badly injured. One policeman had a considerable amount of meat ripped off his leg, the tattered flesh hanging down over his boot like a torn sock. A first-aid man was pouring iodine on the wound and the policeman was saying he wanted brandy and to get back into the street again with a baton.

Johannesburg is tremendous in its humanity. And you can know nothing about human nature if you can see it in only the superficial side of beauty, if you can't see also – and accept and love – that side of it that is just plain terrible.

Johannesburg is asurge with an unquenchable ardour of life. It is fine to think that these steel and concrete skyscrapers have done nothing to dilute that essentially primitive thing, charged with a turgid lust for life, which is the raw spirit of Johannesburg.

They are trying to make Johannesburg respectable. They are trying to make snobs out of us, making us forget who our ancestors were. They are trying to make us lose our sense of pride in the fact that our forebears were a lot of roughnecks who knew nothing about culture and who came here to look for gold. We who are of Johannesburg, we know this spirit that is inside of us, and we don't resent the efforts that are being made to put a collar and tie on this city. Because we know that every so often, when things seem to be going very smoothly on the surface, something will stir in the raw depths of Johannesburg, like the awakening of an old and half-forgotten memory, and the brickbats hurtling down Market Street will be thrown with the same lack of accuracy as when the pioneers of the mining camp did the throwing.

It is out of this zest in life, which Europe hasn't got any

more, that great art will be created. The splendours of true culture. It is significant that art began to decline in France from the time when the authorities started macadamising the main thoroughfares of Paris – so that the populace wouldn't have any more cobbles to tear up to throw.

Some days ago two refugees from Germany, a man and his wife, in reference to the City Hall disturbance, said to me that it was very disgraceful and that that was how it in Germany started. Well, I am not interested about how it in Germany started, but I do know that it started in Johannesburg over 50 years ago, and that it has been going on, at intervals, ever since. And unless we are going to betray the traditions bequeathed to us from our forebears, it will go on as long as we have mine-dumps on our horizon.

"Onsterflike Liefde"

On a lamp-post in front of the entrance to the Male Section of the Johannesburg Fort – as grim a prison as any that there is in the world – there is a placard in red letters announcing the forthcoming presentation of an Afrikaans play with the flaming title, *Onsterflike Liefde* (Undying Love).

It seems a strange juxtaposition. What does one have to make of it? The placard with its flaring declaration that love is "onsterflik". And the prison gate. Two profound human realities. The prison gate stands at the entrance to a subterranean passage below an earthern rampart that is covered significantly enough, with thorny cactus. Thick-stemmed symbolism. The stark aridities of the desert; a path bestrewn with thorns. Years ago, one remembers, those earthen ramparts of the Johannesburg Gaol were covered with a creeper that in the springtime bore a wealth of magenta-hued blossoms which held a singular allurement for members of the public passing down Ameshoff Street. Those bright-coloured flowers were obviously inappropriate and the prison authorities are to be congratulated on that strong insight into the ultimate realities of existence which led them to substitute spiny cactus.

And on a lamp-post, in front of the gaol, in red letters, the placard, *Onsterflike Liefde*. Here there is no incongruity, either. Love is also something that in its deepest essentials suits well with the desert and the thorns of the cactus, and has got very little to do with flowers. Love, in its deeper essentials, I have said. And love also stands as a gateway to those underground labyrinths of the human heart that are, alas, more tortuous than any of the passages twisting underneath the ramparts of the Fort. And more soulfully laden with the solemn intensities of life than are those passages. And more dark.

And passing by that prison gate and that placard on the lamp-post the other day I pondered on a story that in its human qualities would not be in any way different from any one of the thousands of other stories which have had their setting at the entrance gate to the Male Section of the Johannesburg Fort. I thought of the feelings of a girl coming out of that gate from a visit to her man locked behind bars. Perhaps he had already been sentenced. Perhaps he was awaiting trial. That did not matter. What mattered was that when she left she had given him that promise which every woman makes to every man whom she visits in a prison. She would wait for him for ever. Through how many dust-laden centuries have women not made the same promise, in the same tone of voice, under these same circumstances. And in how many different languages. Babylonian, Phrygian, Cappadocian, Visi-Gothic, Sesuto.

And the girl, stepping out on to the pavement in front of the Johannesburg Fort, into sudden sunshine, hearing the prison gate clanging shut behind her, and the remembering or forgetting that her last words were a promise of undying love to a man; and her eyes encounter that placard pasted on the lamp-post, *Onsterflike Liefde.* Whether she is going to break that promise or whether she will keep it seems a matter almost of less significance than the fact that in the words she has just uttered she has become one with all those other women.

Although she doesn't know it, she is no longer an isolated individual. She has become absorbed into a tradition that goes back to before the dawn of civilisation, to before Minos, and to before Assyria, and to before Troy. By the words she has uttered she has become an initiate, whether she likes it or not, into a female fellowship that has a heritage that is both proud and tarnished, and from whose bonds there is no escape. Whether she keeps or breaks the promise she has made to her man makes no difference, for in either event she will merely be acting in accordance with ancient tradition. And if the man behind the bars of the Johannesburg Gaol happens to be the last, so far, of a long line of her lovers, she also happens to be the last, so far, in a long line of a strange and gaudy and battered sisterhood.

So it doesn't matter if this girl steps out on the pavement

and doesn't even notice the placard about *Onsterflike Liefde* because she is busy thinking about some other man. Or if what comes into her mind is the recollection that the pineapple pump of the milkbar counter behind which she works is nearly empty.

It is all part of the same barbarically-ornamented magnificence of life. And who shall say that life is not magnificent?

Old Johannesburg Is Vanishing

What is it all about, a nostalgia for the past? Most people seem to have it. Collecting antiques, revisiting the scenes of one's childhood, standing in awe before an ancient monument – all these are different aspects of sharing in that feeling about time that is bygone and irrecoverable.

I have been having quite a lot of that sort of thing lately. It began with the demolition of the old Magistrates' Courts. At first I felt about this vandalism only a kind of silent fury. The Johannesburg Municipality, I thought. They have got no understanding of Johannesburg, no veneration for this city. I don't suppose, for one thing, that they've got too many genuine Joh'burg old-timers on the Council. Otherwise we wouldn't have every Johannesburg building turned over to a demolition-gang the moment it becomes historical.

If through the centuries the authorities had so little sense of civic responsibility in the towns and cities of Europe, I would like to know how much of their past would be surviving today. About a City Councillor who hasn't got a respect for his city's past, I can feel only one thing: he has got no respect for his own past. Through reasons of modesty, he is not anxious to have his past gone into, in too great detail.

Of course, I can understand, in one way, why there was no public outcry when it was first announced that the old Magistrates' Courts had to come down. It wasn't so with the destruction of the Wanderers or the final closing down of the Standard Theatre. With the Wanderers, especially, there was almost a revolution. But the courts of law, naturally, in their being pulled down, don't leave behind the same kind of a sense of aching void. It is regrettable and all that, the old building having to go . . . the civil and criminal courts . . . built 60 years ago. But the public starts remembering other features of the place. The prisoners' yard was very cramped. And a fact that you couldn't deny was that the toilet facilities were primitive in the extreme. That old blue wash-basin in the corner. And the piece of cracked mirror that you glanced into very hurriedly when your name was called.

No, if you have got to take a realistic view of the matter, then you must admit that there are perhaps certain private reasons – good and sufficient reasons – as to why the Johannesburg public did not protest more vigorously when they heard that the old Magistrates' Courts were going to be knocked down. And perhaps, among the City Councillors who did not raise a finger to stop it, there were a few genuine Joh'burg old-timers . . ."

I went down into the underground vaults of the courthouse, striking matches as I went. A friend and I suggested to the contractor in charge of the demolition that those cellars would be an ideal place to hold a party in. I should say that there will still be time to hold a party until about the end of next month. Since the job of breaking down a building starts at the top, it will take them quite a while yet before they get to the underground cellars. Incidentally, how do you break down an underground cellar? Or do you just leave it undemolished and chuck rubble into it?

In spite of everything, I really believe they shouldn't have destroyed the old building. When they prised off a length of skirting, a paper oblong fluttered out. I picked it up. It was an official envelope, a bit yellowed, with "In Dienst van Zuid-Afrikaanse Republiek" printed on it. No other bits of paper had slipped in anywhere else, as far as I could see, between woodwork and plaster. The old workmen made too good a job of it.

By the way, out of one of the underground vaults they retrieved a board, about six foot by four foot, bearing a lengthy petition neatly painted in red and black letters, drawing attention to certain judicial irregularities alleged to have taken place long ago. The bottom of the board carries the name of the petitioner, one Hall. The accusations he makes against the magisterial bench of that distant past are peculiar both for the violence of the language in which the charges are couched and for the depth of turpitude to which the petitioner believed the said occupants of the bench to have sunk.

I wonder how long Hall got for painting that board in neat red and black letters, and all . . .

Among the people with whom I discussed the breaking down of the old Magistrates' Court was a Johannesburg pioneer. He wasn't very upset about it. "I saw the first sod being turned there for the foundations, when the place was still surrounded with bluegums," he said. "I saw that site as a vacant stand, before they put up the Magistrates' Court. And one of these days I'll see it as a vacant stand again. That's how it goes."

Anyway, because I could remember the old Magistrates' Courts from when I was a child, I felt myself overcome by a sudden urge to renew my acquaintance with other places familiar to me from my earliest years and which I had not glimpsed during an intervening three odd decades.

The result was that, on a hot afternoon, recently, I was walking through the streets of a small Rand town that had not changed much since the early years of this century. The town had expanded outwards. New suburbs had come into existence. The centre of the town, however, had been left almost untouched by progress. I saw on the door of a dilapidated shop an enamel plate, battered but still clearly legible, with the inscription "Closed on Account of the Dust". I remembered spelling out those words when I was first able to read. I remembered that enamel plate well, but very well. And those premises were no longer used as a shop but had been converted into a native lodging house. How can I describe the sense of intimacy that I felt with the "Closed on Account of the Dust" sign? The flies on a mangy dog lying on the pavement seemed to be basking in the sunshine of over thirty years ago. That strip of enamel plate could have meant nothing to the owner of the shop or his heirs, or they would have taken it with them when they moved into more imposing premises. I alone felt an emotion for it.

No, the town had not undergone any substantial alterations. The features that mattered had not changed. Then I strolled out into the veld. I walked for several miles through the long yellow grass, with the sun on my back. There was nothing I recognised. Nothing I saw evoked any memories of the past. I had walked along that road often as a child. But there were no landmarks whereby I could identify this road. I had no means of distinguishing it from any other dusty track winding across any other stretch of veld. The contours of the ground did not help me. I came across a clump of black wattles. But these trees were only of yesterday – not more than twenty years old, you could see: they were long after my time.

I began to get very lonely. Then I got frightened. I wanted to turn back. There lay across the veld that strange, disturbing cast of middle afternoon. I decided to rest by the side of the road before walking back to town. Then among the black wattles, I saw a structure of weathered brick, about four feet high. I knew what it was. I went up closer and examined it. I remembered when they erected that beacon. It was plastered smooth and round. All that was left now was a pile of discoloured brickwork, grim and jagged. A few of the bricks, loosened by time, had fallen off into the yellow grass.

I felt much more lonely, then, in the sunshine by the side of the road. And I was more frightened then ever.

Jam Session

I have seen sensational newspaper photographs of the jiving sessions at the Plaza, as engaged in by Johannesburg's jitter-bugging youth. Girls and boys jiving to the accompaniment of a frenzied orchestra, and talking Americanese, the report said. So I went to have a look.

I must explain, however, that my interest in the United States had been aroused earlier in the same week. And it was in this wise: an old friend of mine, Bert Rawson, had phoned me and made an appointment for a young man who wished to interview me on business. Next day this young man arrived. He came striding into the office with his chin thrust forward and with his hand outstretched and with "U.S.A." in brass letters in his coat lapel. His outer aspect was well matched by his greet-ing, delivered in a nasal twang that I can't hope to convey on paper but of which you can get some sort of idea if you think of an American film about a game of football, or baseball, and you try to recall how the announcer talks through the megaphone. That was how that young fellow addressed me. Naturally, I was bewildered, overpowered, beaten. He could do with me just what he liked. When we separated, I realised that I had accompanied him out of the office, in a sort of a daze, as far as Eloff Street, corner Fox Street. I remembered, then, that I hadn't heard his name properly. So I again asked him his name. But by that time he had got my hand in a firm, pump-handle grip. He shook my arm up and down so vigorously that my hat fell off. So I again failed to catch his name. Because when he said it, he was speaking drawn up to his full height, and looking straight in front of him, while I was bending down on the Eloff Street pavement to retrieve my hat.

"You can't beat these Yanks when it comes to salesman-ship," a man who shares the office with me remarked when I got back.

But I had started thinking. There was something in his act

that was phoney. It was overdone. I remembered that story of O. Henry's about the New York confidence trickster who dressed up like a farmer in order to pass himself off as a simple yokel – and who overdid the make-up by actually sticking hay-seed in his hair.

My suspicions awakened, I phoned Bert Rawson. "That young fellow you sent over to me," I said, "what part of the Free State does he come from?" And Bert told me. Trompsburg, I think he said.

But it was quite easy for me, really. You see, I knew that no Yank could have a handshake like that. You can acquire so robust, so paralysing a grip only through prolonged spells of holding the plough into the stony soil of the Free State high-veld.

Anyway, the point about all the foregoing is that it is compara-tively easy for anybody that wants to become an American. And you can't help thinking slightingly about something that's not hard to get. Consequently, when I read in the Press that the Joh'burg jivesters at the Plaza were highly Americanised, that fact did not help to prejudice me in their favour.

I felt very self-conscious when I arrived in front of the Plaza. A long line of rhythm-fan youths and maidens stood queued up in front of the box-office for their tickets – one-and-a-penny inc. tax. I did not mind forking out my one and one. But I shivered at the thought of having to stand in that queue. I was afraid they would think I was also going to jive and that they would, accordingly laugh. So I went up to Jack Bloom and said I was Press, and would he give the doorman the nod to pass me in free. O.K., Jack Bloom said. You see, the whole show was like that, just bristling with Americanisms. Inside, later on, I even heard somebody use the word "guy" – a familiar term signifying an adult male person.

The orchestra played a hot tune called *Torpedo Junction* and a young fellow in striped trousers came on to the stage accompanied by a girl in a black skirt and grey top. They jived. Then the band played a hotter tune called *Cross-Eyed Flo-Flo-Florrie* and a young man in hospital blues accompanied by a girl in a black skirt and a grey top came on. The man did not jive too well; the girl was better than the girl who came on first. Then the band played a hot tune called *Ave Maria* and a young man in plus-fours and a girl in black skirt and a grey top started jitterbugging. The girl was terrific – much better than her two predecessors, I thought. Only then I discovered that it was the same girl right through, and that she seemed better each time because she was warming up her job.

After that the band played more hot tunes and more and more couples climbed on to the stage, which eventually got so crowded that several members of the orchestra got pushed off, and all present, meaning those on the stage and those off, were stamping and clapping and perhaps even screaming a little. When I say everybody, I would like to explain that I don't include the doorman. I don't think I heard him scream.

Ah, youth.

I am glad that I attended that jam session. The jivesters bumped their behinds against the stage scenery and didn't seem to mind. They jumped and wriggled and kicked in wild abandon, just like you see in the films, but not so neatly, of course; not so hotcha and hepcat. Nevertheless, they were, on a Johannesburg cinema stage, reproducing all the latest swing stuff imported straight from America.

But they weren't near as good as the couple of kaffir girls, that I once saw jiving in a yard in End Street. And they didn't even know that they were jiving. They were only dancing to the old rhythms of Africa. And they also sold skokiaan.

Shanty Town

Situated on the slope of a hill about ten miles outside the City of Johannesburg is a township whose expanding dimensions should soon entitle it to the prestige of being termed a city, also. At present it is known as Shanty Town.

Shanty Town today contains several thousand shacks, each consisting of a rough framework of poles covered over with sacking and each housing a native family. Here let it be explained that our visit took place in bright sunshine. It was a pleasant morning and as far as the writer was concerned the visit was not made in any spirit of sociological crusading, which seems to demand of the individual a preconceived righteous indignation against the existing economic order – so that whatever is experienced and observed gets fitted into appropriate and ready-made emotions.

Consequently, where this picture of actual conditions in Shanty Town may appear to fall short will be in respect of its deliberate avoidance of the obvious. Stories of squalor, told with a consistent drabness, in grey shadows unrelieved by the light of imagination, tend, in their ultimates, to pall. The heart gets tired of the same old note struck over and over again. It is not in human nature for one's feelings to be kept at the same pitch of intensity – whether the feelings are of pity or of righteous wrath – all the time. There is such a thing as tedium. And if it is not polite to yawn at a platitude it is, at all events, natural.

For this reason this article will be confined to an objective description of an interesting little town, healthfully situated on a hillside, and it will be left to the reader to make his own comments, such as "dastardly" or "delightful", depending alike on his own subjective reactions and his capacity for reading between the lines.

What first struck the writer, who has considerable practical knowledge of constructive engineering, was that two distinct types of building material are employed in the erection of the shanties. Most of the residential abodes are covered over with mealie sacks. A few – and these belonging obviously to the more aristocratic section – have their walls and roof constructed of sugar-pockets bearing the trademark of Messrs. Hulett. Close examination shows that the hessian in a sugar-pocket is of finer texture and better woven than that in a mealie-bag, and is consequently a superior building material. It keeps out the elements better.

Each shack is numbered in some dark-coloured paint. These numbers run into thousands, thereby affording a rough-and-ready means of computing the population of the place. It also makes it easier for the postman on his round to deliver correspondence and newspapers. One does not imagine that the residents of Shanty Town get troubled much with tradesmen's circulars, however. Although an enterprising house-agent can, if he so desires, strike an incongruous note by circularising the area with printed literature about "Why pay Rent? Let Us show You how to Build your Own House."

There is little about these hessian-covered shacks that is in conflict with the fundamental laws of architecture, which are that a building should be planned in accordance with the purpose for which it is required, that it should carry no ornamentation that is outside of this purpose, and that its design should be guided by the type of material that is employed. From an aesthetic point of view the architecture of Shanty Town can therefore be described as not undignified. About none of these shacks is there that false attempt at drama that makes Park Station an eyesore.

And when a native woman told us that she was suffering from chest pains as a result of her hut having been drenched during the recent rains, and that most of the people there were suffering from various illnesses contracted through sleeping under soaked blankets, her complaints were not based on artistic grounds but on the simple scientific fact that sacking is porous and lets in the water in the rainy season.

But from the point of view of pure architecture there is not much wrong with these dwellings. The washed-out yellows of the hessian roofs and walls blend prettily with the grass of the South African veld in mid-winter. Washed-out yellow against bleached fawn. Pretty. And veld-coloured huts built close to the soil seem much more appropriate for South African conditions than skyscrapers and blocks of flats. The shacks in the main street of Shanty Town seem to express the true spirit of Africa in a way that the buildings in Eloff Street do not.

But all these things are merely by the way. For that matter, one feels that if a number of Kalahari Bushmen were brought to Johannesburg on a visit to a fashionable block of city flats they would go back to the desert with strong feelings about the white man's degradation. "Like living in an anthill," they would say. "Squalor." "Unhygienic." "Like pigs." "And you ought to see some of those pictures they hang on their walls . . . just too awful."

What was most interesting about Shanty Town was its human side. One felt in the place the warmth of a strong and raw life. Deplorable though their economic circumstances were, there was about these men and woman and children a sense of life that had no frustration in it. A dark vitality of the soil. An organic power for living that one imagined nothing in this world could take away. Was there anything about us, about this party of white visitors, that the residents of Shanty Town could genuinely envy? In our hearts the answer was, no.

The replies which the natives returned to our questions were prideful. Their attitude was a lesson in breeding. They resented our presence, in the way that any proud person resents the intrusion into his affairs of curiosity or patronage. And they received us with that politeness that shames. We wanted to know what had happened to Mapanza, the headman who had fought against the humiliating introduction of soup kitchens, and they informed us, with grave dignity, that "he was not there". Although everybody knew, what we subsequently learnt from a policeboy, that Mapanza was in gaol.

Whatever information we got we received from the policeboy: from the side of the authorities and not from the side of the residents. And when we left, a native woman asked us if we were going to send blankets. It was a perfect snub, whose imputation could not be lost even on the most obtuse. A duchess could not have administered it better.

Whatever ill-effects detribalisation may have had on the natives, it has done nothing, judging from what is happening in Shanty Town, to the stateliness of their aristocracy. Living under what are nothing less than ghastly conditions, deprived, apparently, of even the barest necessities of human existence, the inhabitants of Shanty Town are displaying, in the face of adversity, a sublime courage that goes far beyond questions of economics and sociology.

If life is spirit, what the natives of Shanty Town bear about them is not poverty but destiny.

Round the Galleries in July

Activity in the Johannesburg art world is, at this time of the year, at a standstill. This fact was brought home to me rather forcibly when, on my monthly round of the galleries, I found that the only show that was new was the Diederick During exhibition at the Constantia. At one place I visited there was a native in charge of the pictures. The boss had gone to Durban for the July, he informed me. I suppose you've got to be a bit of a gambler in this line of business, I thought. What you lose on the swings you make up on the roundabouts. If you can pick the winner of the Durban July, then it doesn't matter so much if a couple of long-haired painters that you thought were Van Goghs turn out to be also-rans.

You can make it up on the racecourse.

Talking about long-haired artists, it's amazing how many of them we seem to be getting in Johannesburg these days. Why, I can remember the time, not so many years ago – only about a quarter of a century or thereabouts – when an artist in Johannesburg was very much of a phenomenon. An artist in Johannesburg was something so unusual that people would go miles out of their way to see him. Not to buy his pictures, of course. Nothing like that. But just to go and have a look at him. There was an artist living here called Quilter, I remember. He was a Hungarian who wanted to go to America. Or an Australian who wanted to go to Hungary. I forgot which. But I remember that he was a sensation, just because he stuck bits of real paint on a piece of real canvas, and because he had a real easel and a real palette, exactly like you see in pictures of artists. It was, of course, all very romantic and thrilling and arty and proper.

And, needless to say, nobody ever bought one of his pictures. Good lord, you didn't feel that way about him. With the years, I have lost touch with Quilter. Maybe he did go to Siberia, after all, or Bulgaria, or the Argentine, or Portuguese East

Africa, or wherever it was that he wanted to go to. Maybe he has sold a picture, too.

Another artist – and about the only one, as far as I can recall, for nobody ever saw Gwelo Goodman painting a mine dump and Amschewitz was regarded as being more of a Journalist than a True Artist – who lived in Johannesburg in the old days was Emily I. Fern. Many years ago I saw her, with her easel erected on a pavement just off Kerk Street, painting a picture of the New Law Courts in the semi-translucent light of early dawn. Because it was so unusual a sight for Johannesburg – a lady artist doing a spot of painting on the pavement – a little knot of Joh'burg citizens had grouped themselves around the easel. The comments they made were not all favourable. A few other citizens, more knowledgeable where this sort of thing was concerned, had placed themselves about half-way be-tween the artist and the law courts. The poses they struck were not unimpressive. It was obvious that their idea was that, well, seeing they were standing there, anyway, the artist would have to put them into the picture.

Whether they appeared in the picture in the capacity of legal luminaries or of accused persons out on bail was a matter that, I suppose, was quite immaterial to them. That was old Joh'burg for you.

Strangely enough, I saw that same painting, again, many years later. In fact, quite recently. I saw it in Emily Fern's stu-dio. No, it hadn't been sold. There, as I have remarked, is old Joh'burg for you.

The transition of Johannesburg, from a mining camp to occu-pying the position of the accepted cultural, literary and artistic centre of the African Continent (and vis-a-vis Europe, Africa, although infinitely older, is at least not played out) – brings with it many paradoxes. Much of poetry and a good helping of eternity.

I believe that, today, a Johannesburg artist, who will stick it out in Johannesburg, and will win out in Johannesburg, will win.

Another art gallery I walked into, the woman told me that they weren't putting on an exhibition, because the art-buying public had all gone to Durban. She didn't say where the boss was.

Hoboes

Arising out of the somewhat sensational articles at the moment appearing in the local press (both English and Afrikaans) on the subject of Johannesburg's hoboes, and the efforts being made by the municipal welfare society to bring about their rehabilitation, I felt that I would like to conduct a few investigations into the question on my own behalf, especially when I read a sub-leader in an Afrikaans daily on the superior class of person nowadays being attracted to the ranks of the sherry-gang. Accordingly, I got into touch with a number of social welfare officials, who all assured me that the newspaper reports to the effect that lots of regular bums around the City Hall had at one time been blue-blooded members of the world of fashion were grossly exaggerated.

I was informed that there was no truth in the assertion that among the hoboes sleeping in our alleys and parks were several former Cabinet Ministers and ex-Mayors of Johannesburg. I was glad to hear that. The hoboes are a sufficiently forlorn and friendless section of the community. Let us not seek to malign them further.

Anyway, I pursued my enquiries, and one thing led to another, and eventually I was able to interview a lady social welfare worker who for the past two years has made a special and detailed study of the ways of Johannesburg's bums. She has amassed a large stack of case histories, and during the course of an hour's conversation she imparted to me a good deal of information that I found both amusing and instructive.

The lady informed me that she started off life as a journalist. And it was while she was working on a newspaper that she first encountered the real hobo type.

"Yes," I agreed with her, "I don't know what it is about journalism. But it's always the hobo type that you see working in newspaper offices."

But she said that she didn't mean it that way exactly.

She went on to talk about bums and their ways, mentioning the fact that a hobo's footwear consists in general of a pair of tattered sandshoes, padded with newspapers and tied to his insteps with pieces of string. She once got a hobo fixed up with a job as steward on the railway. The S.A.R. supplied the hobo with the regulation waiter's suit. He reported for duty, next day punctually, on the Cape Mail. And he looked quite all right, too, in his dinner-jacket and black trousers and carrying a tray. But his tackies, reinforced with string and newspapers, formed the subject of a good deal of ill-natured gossip in the dining saloon.

My informant told me an interesting story of a man social welfare investigator who took a deep and sincere interest in his work and even went so far as to dress up as a hobo and to join the bums in John Ware Park. He was able in this way to gain very valuable information and to compile a number of exceptionally interesting case histories. He actually lived with the hoboes and even joined them in what they called "putting the straight bite" on passing pedestrians, in order to get money for wine. He learnt a great deal in that way. This social welfare investigator was last reported as having been seen in the Standerton district, heading south.

He was said to be trolling a woodland lay.

Questioned by me as to the approximate number of hoboes in the Johannesburg area, this woman social worker said that it was difficult to form an estimate because the hoboes moved about so much. She said that the Welfare Department had on several occasions sent out a number of investigators to try and get some sort of a rough count. My informant herself was stationed in the environs of the City Hall every day for a week, and while she was able to record having spotted several hundred bums during that period, she wasn't certain if they were all hoboes, and if some of them were not going into the City Hall to work.

A further difficulty in the way of taking an exact census of Johannesburg's hoboes, my informant said, was brought about by the fact that a certain percentage of them were always, at any given time, in gaol – nearly always on charges of being drunk and disorderly. They could also be convicted of vagrancy and begging, she said, but arrests on these charges were rare, because the hobo had apparently developed a sort of sixth sense when it came to recognising a policeman, even when in plain clothes.

"You don't mean when a hobo is in plain clothes, but when a policeman is?" I asked, to make sure.

"Yes," she replied. "I don't know how it is, but they can always tell a policeman no matter how he is dressed. It is a mystery to me how they do it."

"Say, lady –" I began, and I started leaning forward confidentially, and I was going to tell her, too, how you can spot a john when he's still two blocks away. But I am glad that I pulled myself up in time.

Anyway, there's no mystery about it. As O. Henry explained long ago, you don't need to look at a man's feet, even, to find out if he's from headquarters; you can tell right away by his chin and his eyes.

From there, the conversation naturally drifted to a discussion of the slang expressions used by hoboes, and my informant came to light with certain information that was new to me. Every hobo, she said, cherishes a secret dream of being one day respectable and working in a regular job. And whenever a social welfare worker approaches a hobo and talks to him along these lines, explaining what can be done for him in the way of getting him a regular occupation, the hobo is very much interested. And the way the hobo gives expression to his sense of pleasure is by means of a phrase that is well known in the argot of the underworld. The hobo says, simply and feelingly, "That will be the day."

Shortly afterwards – having first enquired from the social welfare worker as to whether she did not perhaps have a muffler or a pair of socks that she could spare – I took my departure.

On my way back to the office I spoke to a hobo I saw on a bench in that little park near the station.

210

"What's the bumming game like these days?" I asked him.

"The going is hook," he replied. "It's these social workers they got now. They're driving me nuts. There's one social welfare worker that we calls Flatface. Now, you take his case history . . ."

Humour and Wit

How shall we define the wayward and mysterious and outcast thing that we term humour – that is forever a pillar-to-post fugitive from the stern laws of reality, and yet forms so intimate a part of (and even embodies) all truth about which there is an eternal ring?

There isn't so much humour in the world today as there was of yore, I think, and through the realms of culture there do not sweep those gusts of great laughter that blew the lamp smoke away from thought and left behind an intoxication. The material for splendid mirth is still here, of course; right in our midsts. Turn but a stone and the diamonds coruscate. But the man who could make out of this material a supremely godlike brand of jesting we seem not to have with us more.

Lots of people have tried to analyse humour: writers, comedians, clergymen, psychologists, undertakers, political cartoonists, crooks, prison superintendents – in fact, all sorts of men in whose private or professional lives humour plays an important role. But I have never come across any attempt at trying to explain what it is that makes us laugh, that has impressed me very much. You can work out what are the important ingredients that go towards the compounding of that rare and very subtle thing that stirs the risible faculties. But that doesn't get you anywhere. You can analyse the elements that embrace laughter, but you can't make anybody laugh with your analysis.

The same thing with those distinctions that people draw between humour and wit. Is there any difference? I don't know. If that rather generally accepted, rough-and-ready attempt at classification holds water – namely, that humour is born out of the emotions and wit springs from the intellect, then I would naturally be prone to look upon wit as being, to some extent, an intruder, I, who am by nature suspicious of the intellect, fancying that in its dark recesses there lurks a specious cunning whose purpose is to gloss over with trickery the soul's deficiencies.

With this deep-seated distrust of the intellect, therefore, I would be inclined to move warily within the domain of wit, if the above-mentioned definition were correct. But, funnily enough, I don't think there is much truth in it. When something makes me laugh I would have to think twice if I am laughing intellectually or if it is just low, moron joy. And if I had to pause in order to reflect on this problem, I wouldn't want to go on laughing any more.

Humour we find all over the place. But with writers of humour (at least with the kind of humour that appeals to me) it seems to be different. You seem to find them at particular times in particular places. The Elizabethans had a sense of humour that I can respond to as readily as to a backveld joke about rinderpest and drought. And I regard Shakespeare as the greatest humorist I have ever struck. And the singular thing about it is that he seems to me to have been a humorist primarily in the literary sense (as the Americans of the last century were humorists primarily in the literary sense), for his jests seem to have a spontaneous magic in the form of the written word that they lack spoken, dramatised. Because I have always derived much more pleasure from reading Shakespeare's humour than from seeing it on the stage. Perhaps I have never yet seen Shakespeare, when he is being funny, properly acted.

But with the exception of the Elizabethans, there have been no English writers who have risen to such dazzling heights of fantasy or have reached to genius through such an utter abandonment of the spirit, that I would be willing to make for them the claim that they should be admitted, without reservation, to wearing of the true humorist's garland. There are a large number that I would be willing to accept, making allowances for this and for that. But when it comes to my responses to humour, I prefer to be with those for whom I have to make no concessions.

And here I feel that I am in godly company: the American

humorists of the last century. Mark Twain and those who preceded him, and those who came after, too, some of them. I feel there has never in the whole history of the world been anything so shocking, so sublime, and truthful and starlike and inspired, as what those men wrote who contributed to that immortal beauty of literature that comprises American humour. It began shortly after the American War of Independence, this particular expression of a literary spirit whose goal was the awakening of gigantic laughter . . .

(I had reached to this point, in the writing of this present article, when I was summoned from my desk by a telephone call. A gentleman at the other end of the line informed me that he was the City Fire Department, and that my house was on fire. Naturally, I was perturbed, thinking of all my unpublished and uninsured odes and things going up in flame. The gentleman on the line then informed me that he was not the Fire Department, after all, but that he was one, Jumbo, and that he had been informed that I was engaged in writing on Humour, and how did I like this false alarm as an example of refined humour? But I felt that the laugh wasn't on me, after all: one day I am going to publish those uninsured odes.)

By the time of the Civil War this new kind of humour (new, not in its essence but in its strength and stark objectivity) had blossomed into quite unimaginable beauty; and it lasted, in the hands of one or two men of genius, right into the early years of the present century. But for as long as a generation before that it had already begun to manifest, deep within its structure, the elements of a dark decay. The writers stopped creating humour for its own sake. They began to apply this powerful weapon to the serving of causes that a creative artist can't believe in. In this respect O. Henry, coming in right at the other end of the epoch, kept his art untainted in a way that Mark Twain, ultimately, didn't.

When the laughter gets forced, the humour dies, and you can see this process beginning with work in the later writings of Artemus Ward, Josh Billings, Bill Nye, Petroleum V. Nasby, and several others, including, as I have said, Mark Twain. (Witness the decline in power between Mark Twain's earlier Mississippi sketches and the stuff he turned out a quarter of a century later – his pathetically inept *Joan of Arc*, for instance.) His genius, of course, did not decay. Only, his art suffered immeasurably through his seeking to make it subserve his own (totally mistaken) ideas of himself as a literary figure.

There is nothing that you can detect more easily, or that falls more jarringly on the aesthetic sense, than a false laugh.

But there were also writers of this epoch who remained artistically true to themselves. Amongst them I can think, offhand, of Max Adler. (He is a gorgeous humorist; free, romantic, superbly imaginative.) And, of course, Bret Harte. There were giants in those days.

American humour today is all right, of course, as far as I am concerned. Only it has lost its pristine vigour, its startlingly accurate insight into the strengths and frailties of human nature, its divine extravagance. It has lost its human genius; it has run to seed; it has grown thin.

I have devoted so much space to a consideration of American humour because I can understand it better than any humour that has ever come out of Europe, and because I regard it, even in decay, as a mighty and unparalleled manifestation. I can't write humorously about American humour.

There are, of course, lots of kinds of humour that I can't understand at all. I have never yet been able to see anything in *Punch*. (Perhaps *Punch* isn't a funny paper.) And I have never been able to laugh at what have been held out to me as even the most brilliant examples of Cockney wit. (Perhaps Cockney wit, also, is not meant to be amusing. Again I don't know. I can catch about Cockney wit only a devastating quickness. I can sense in it none of that warmth that is the very life-blood of true humour.)

All the ordinary attempts at evaluating the significance of humour in terms of its social use and its psycho-physiological functioning seem, of necessity, to have to end in sterility. Humour is something that stands apart from these things. I feel that to get at the true essence of humour, it must be approached from the side of the eternities, where it stands as some sort of a battered symbol of man's more direct relationship with God.

In the world's cultural development humour came on the scene very late. And that is the feeling that I have always had about humour, ultimately. That it is one of mankind's most treasured possessions, one of the world's richest cultural jewels. But that humour came amongst us when the flowers were already fading. And that it came too late.

Stephen Leacock

The death of Stephen Leacock a month or so ago brought to an end a great tradition of American humour which, over the course of more than a century, bequeathed to the world a noble literary heritage.

There were giants in those days. One feels that American humour in the hands of its present-day exponents has run to seed, wisecracks and flashy brilliance having superseded that spontaneous laughter of the heart in that world where Mark Twain was king, and where Josh Billings, Artemus Ward, Bret Harte (in his *Condensed Novels*) and Max Adler were lordly courtiers. Much of O. Henry was in the same tradition. Ambrose Bierce, in the essentials of his spirit was no different.

But one feels that this line has ended with Stephen Leacock. Gone are those incredible fantasies made up out of hyperbole and meiosis. Ossa will be piled upon Pelion no more.

Wit, which is manufactured by the intellect, and is easy to produce, has replaced humour, which belongs with the emotions, and is a very rare thing in the world, and is as precious a thing as poetry, to which it is closely akin. Humour is the brother; poetry is the sister.

George Bernard Shaw once proclaimed in an inspired moment that the New World has produced only two geniuses: Edgar Allan Poe and Mark Twain. These two are, incidentally, more than enough. Two sublime spirits of light. Edgar Allan Poe was a poet of a stature overshadowing all other literary figures from his own times until today; it is only within the past few years that his true eminence has come to be appreciated. How a raw young country like America came to produce a poet like Edgar Allan Poe is more inexplicable than anything in all of his *Tales of Mystery and Imagination*.

Edgar Allan Poe was not part of any perceptible American literary current. But Mark Twain was. As early as the beginning of last century a number of American writers, including a man who had been a general in the War of Independence, were writing letters and sketches in which were struck that authentic note of humour sprung from the soil that reached its highest level in *The Innocents Abroad*.

And the distinguishing characteristic of the American humorists in the grand manner was that they could all write. Their literature was created out of their feeling for humour, out of their sense of contrast, to which the way of life itself in the opening up of a vast continent provided a magnificent background. But in writing up the material of the life around them they produced great literature. Their style was polished; their feeling for language was exquisite. As models of literary style the great American humorists repay study.

Alas, that a splendid era in the literature of the world has ended.